THE BEAUTY TREATMENT HANDBOOK

THE
BEAUTY
TREATMENT
HANDBOOK

THE FACTS ABOUT
OVER 30 DIFFERENT
BEAUTY TREATMENTS

Linda Zeff

CHANCELLOR
PRESS

Copyright © 1988 by Linda Zeff

First published in 1988 by
Judy Piatkus (Publishers) Limited

This 1994 edition published by
Chancellor Press, an imprint of
Reed Consumer Books Limited,
Michelin House, 81 Fulham Road,
London SW3 6RB
and Auckland, Melbourne, Singapore and Toronto

A CIP catalogue record for this book is
available at the British Library

ISBN 1 85152 562 9

Designed by Paul Sanders

Phototypeset in 10/12 pt Linotron Palatino by
Phoenix Photosetting, Chatham
Printed & Bound in Great Britain at
The Bath Press, Avon

DEDICATION

To Annette and Sweet Pea

ACKNOWLEDGEMENTS

I would like to thank the following people for their invaluable help and advice: Koula Georgiou for filling in all the gaps in my knowledge of the beauty world, and for helping me check the manuscript; the Nayar family and their terrific staff at Mystique Health and Beauty Clinic in Hampstead Garden Suburb for introducing me to all kinds of treatments, and for their continuous support and encouragement; Kenneth Morris and Barbara Tate of the London Institute of Beauty Culture; Kaisa Tuhino-Brown and Erika Williams of the Scholl shop in Knightsbridge; Kristin Centofanti of Slendertone; Stephen Purdew, Kim Holland and their staff at Henlow Grange Health Farm; Clare Maxwell-Hudson; Marian Shearn of Thalgo; Antoinette Gordon and Eleanor Church of The Katherine Corbett Clinic in London; Fridolin Davis and Karen Lelyweld of Fridolin's Beauty Clinic in Pinner; Marie Caudwell of René Guinot; Nicky Lyon-Maris and Lesley Woolley of Clarins; David Lieber of DeCleor; *Health and Beauty Salon* magazine; and finally, Michelle Baker, whose offer of help with the typing helped me sleep at night!

The author and publisher have made every effort to ensure that all the information in this book is accurate at the time of going to press. However, no directory can ever be completely up to date – addresses may change and prices will fluctuate.

CONTENTS

THE TREATMENTS

FOREWORD

If you're the kind of person who feels intimidated by white-coated therapists in beauty salons, this book is for you. It's the 'first-time buyer's' guide to those beauty treatments you've always wondered about but never plucked up the courage to try.

It will tell you exactly what each treatment involves – from what clothes you'll be expected to remove, to how long the treatments will take and how often you should have them – as well as alerting you to reasons why you shouldn't try certain treatments, and giving you some convincing reasons why you might want to try certain others!

I can't, unfortunately, guarantee that every treatment will do for you what therapists claim, and I would advise you to check with your doctor if you're in *any* doubt about your health. But I can assure you – from first-hand experience – that most treatments are very pleasant and have a wonderfully relaxing effect. And if you're relaxed, you'll certainly look and feel good – and that's what beauty is all about!

Linda Zeff
February 1987

MAN APPEAL

Even though most of these treatments could be called 'beauty' treatments, and involve visits to salons, men would also benefit from them. See the rating at the end of each treatment to see if it's worth encouraging your husband/boyfriend father/son to try it.

PLEASURE RATING

To give you some idea of which treatments are purely treats, and which involve some amount of discomfort – though no treatments in this book are actually painful – see the pleasure rating at the end of each one. Here is what they mean.

+5 Delightful! Worth having for relaxation alone
+4 Very pleasant
+3 Pleasant
+2 Fairly pleasant
+1 More pleasant than unpleasant
  0 Neither pleasant nor unpleasant
−1 Not particularly unpleasant, but not the best way of relaxing
−2 May involve small amount of discomfort
−3 Involves some discomfort for most people
−4 Involves fair amount of discomfort for most people
−5 Least comfortable treatment for most people – though results usually worth suffering for!

An
Introduction To
The Beauty World

If you've never been into a beauty salon before, you may be wondering what's involved, whether therapists have any formal training, and how you can be sure you're getting the best treatment possible. The following information should help.

WHAT IS A BEAUTY THERAPIST?

A beauty therapist, as opposed to a beauty consultant (usually someone trained by a cosmetic house to work in department stores, selling its goods), must undergo a long period of extensive training before she is let loose on the public. She will be trained at a technical college or private beauty school, and must pass exams in everything from anatomy to the actual application of treatments. And you can be certain that she herself has tried every treatment she will give you, even electrolysis – in training, therapists work on each other's legs!

If you're in any doubt about a therapist, ask to see her qualifying certificates. They are usually displayed in the salon anyway.

You should always feel confident about a therapist's qualifications. It's advisable to see if she (or her salon manager) is a member of BABTAC – the British Association of Beauty Therapy and Cosmetology. Therapists cannot join this professional organisation unless they have recognised external qualifications.

BABTAC, which was formed in 1977 by an amalgamation of the Association of Beauty Therapists (established since 1958) and the Society of Applied Cosmetology (established since 1966), has a very strict code of conduct, and makes sure members maintain their salons to an agreed standard, as well as insuring them against accidents from negligence.

BABTAC has over 3,000 members and will be able to recommend a local therapist or beauty salon if you contact:

Mrs D. Parkes,
The British Association of Beauty Therapy and Cosmetology, Suite 5, Wolseley House, Oriel Road, Cheltenham, Glos. GL50 1TH. Tel: 0242 570284.

WHAT CERTIFICATES SHOULD YOU LOOK FOR?
CIBTAC   This is the BABTAC exam held by private schools and a number of technical colleges. The minimum requirements laid down for the whole course – which covers facials, body treatments and electrolysis – are 800 hours of study, which usually take a minimum of six months to complete.

A basically British examination board, CIBTAC exams are now held at schools overseas, and its diploma is becoming more widely accepted. It is the fastest growing of all the examination boards, and held over 1,000 different examinations in 1986.

(Full details from Mrs D. Parkes, at BABTAC as above.)

CIDESCO   This qualification is awarded mainly in private schools and is an extension of the CIBTAC course. CIDESCO is the best known qualification in the world. The course has been going for about 40 years, with schools in about fifteen countries all following the same pattern.

The board of directors of CIDESCO, which is based in Zurich, includes representatives of half a dozen countries. Major decisions are made at an annual congress which is known as the General Assembly, a kind of mini-United Nations.

(Full details from Mrs D. Parkes, at BABTAC as above.)

CITY AND GUILDS   This is the main course taken by technical colleges.

(Details from *City and Guilds London Institute*, 46 Britannia Street, London WC1 9RG. Tel: 01–278 2468.)

ITEC (International Therapy Examination Council)   Its examinations are taken in both technical colleges and private schools.

(Details from *The Secretariat, International Therapy Examination Council*, 16 Avenue Place, Harrogate, North Yorks. HG2 7PJ. Tel: 0423 880193.)

INTERNATIONAL HEALTH AND BEAUTY COUNCIL Certificate worked for in technical colleges and a few private schools.

(Details from *The International Health and Beauty Council*, 109 Felpham Road, Felpham, West Sussex PO22 7PW. Tel: 0243 860320.)

Incidentally, therapists *do* fail exams – the examiners are very strict. The most often failed exam is electrolysis.

WHAT SHOULD YOU LOOK FOR IN A THERAPIST?

1. She should be friendly and make you feel comfortable. The main benefit of any beauty treatment is that you'll come away feeling relaxed and happy – and you can't expect to relax if a therapist doesn't put you at your ease.

2. She should take time to find out about you and your skin before recommending any course of treatment.

3. She should be clean and neat: Her fingernails should be spotlessly clean, varnish-free and short (otherwise she may scratch you); her overall and hair should also be immaculate.

4. She should explain what every treatment involves and be able to answer your questions adequately.

5. She should take the trouble to check regularly that you are warm and comfortable enough during treatments.

6. She should be able to recommend products you can use at home, and check that you are carrying out the most suitable beauty routine.

WHAT SHOULD YOU LOOK FOR IN A SALON?

1. It should have a pleasant and relaxing atmosphere. If you're simply rushed into a cubicle, given a treatment, and hurried out again, try a different salon.

2. It should be spotlessly clean. Ask to be shown round before you have treatment at a new salon. Look to see that the cubicles are tidy, any towels look clean and fresh, and that there's a shower (especially if you're planning to have a sauna or sunbed treatment).

3. It should keep good record cards, and refer to them regularly.

4. It should be able to provide somewhere safe for you to leave your handbag and jewellery if necessary. However, you will usually be able to keep them with you in the cubicle.

5. It is advisable that it is a member of BABTAC (see page 11).

WHY DO YOU NEED A CONSULTATION?

Before you have any treatment in a salon you must spend some time with the therapist so that she can find out about you, your needs, your medical history, etc, and so that you can find out about her and her salon.

If you've never been to a beauty salon before, you might be amazed (and perhaps annoyed at first) at the amount of information the therapist needs to know about you. But it's very important, both for your safety – the more she knows about you, the less chance of her recommending, or allowing you to try out, beauty treatments that might be harmful – and for her peace of mind.

And a good therapist is one who insists on a free consultation before she gives you any kind of treatment. So always allow a little extra time before your first treatment.

Bear in mind, too, that you may fancy a certain treatment that, say, a friend has recommended. But it might not be the best one for you. A trained therapist will be able to give you help and advice that your best friend can't.

WHAT KIND OF QUESTIONS MIGHT YOU BE ASKED DURING A CONSULTATION?

1. About your medical history: whether you have had any major operations; whether you are on any medication (including the contraceptive pill); whether you have any reason to suspect you may be pregnant, etc. It is vital you answer all questions honestly.

2. Your doctor's name and telephone number: the therapist may want to contact your doctor if she is in any doubt about whether you should have a particular treatment.

3. Your age, weight, height, etc.

4. Personal details such as whether you have any children, the kind of work you do. From these she may be able to determine the reasons for, say, the state of your skin. If you work in a centrally heated office, for example, it could explain dryness.

AROMATHERAPY

The Facts

WHAT IS IT?

Aromatherapy is exactly what its name implies – a therapy with aromas. Essential oils are massaged into the face and body to promote a feeling of relaxation or to help cure certain ills.

The oils are completely natural and are extracted from the roots, stalks, leaves, flowers or fruit of plants and sometimes from the rind of fruits. They have all kinds of healing properties, but it's the aromas that are most beneficial from a beauty point of view since they will help to relax you.

The term 'aromatherapy' was coined by a French scientist called Professor Gattefossé at the end of the last century. It means the therapeutic use of odiferous substances obtained from flowers, plants and aromatic shrubs, by inhaling them or applying them to the skin. Aromatherapy was used extensively in World War II to help heal wounds and scars, and later a French biochemist named Marguerite Maury introduced it to the beauty world.

The massage used in aromatherapy is based on Chinese massage, and massage of the connective tissue (tissue that's alive and connected to muscles and nerve endings). It's not just an ordinary body massage – it's a top-to-toe treatment, dealing with the whole of your body.

Once massaged into your skin, with a carrier oil such as soya oil, essential oils will not only seep into the skin to relax you but will also penetrate into the bloodstream. As a result, the oils can be used to treat anything from depression to rheumatism, as well as relieving tension and promoting healthy skin.

WHERE CAN YOU TRY IT?
- At beauty salons
- At health farms and clubs
- At alternative medicine centres
- At aromatherapy clinics

HOW MUCH SHOULD IT COST?
Around £15 to £30. The treatment is expensive because of the cost of the essential oils. The essences are found only in tiny amounts, and have to be painstakingly extracted. It takes 2,000 lb (900 kg) of rose petals to produce just 1 lb (450 g) of rose oil, for example. And, unfortunately, synthetic substances do not have the same effect.

If you can't afford regular treatments, why not see if your local aromatherapy school takes models?

HOW OFTEN SHOULD YOU HAVE IT?
Once a week or once every two weeks at first, to let the aromatherapist get used to your body. Ideally you should have regular sessions after that. The more often you can afford treatments, the longer-lasting the effects, especially if you continue treatments at home.

However, since it is very expensive, you might simply want to have a treatment every now and again as a treat (perhaps at the beginning of every season)!

HOW LONG SHOULD A TREATMENT TAKE?
Between one and one and a half hours.

DO TRY AROMATHERAPY:
1. if you're tense and under strain.
2. a couple of days before a special occasion. Even if you usually have a lifeless, sallow complexion, you should find your skin will glow beautifully.

BUT **DON'T** TRY AROMATHERAPY WITHOUT CHECKING FIRST WITH YOUR DOCTOR:
1. if you're pregnant. However, you could have a lighter treatment, and stretch marks may be prevented if you use the right oils at home.
2. if you've just had an operation.

3. if you have severe heart trouble.
4. if you have varicose veins.
5. if you suffer from obesity.
6. if you have very high blood pressure.
7. if you have cancer.
8. if you are very nervous, or elderly.

(For all the above, lighter or different treatments are available, provided your doctor agrees. The therapist may, however, recommend oils you could use at home.)

HOW CAN YOU TELL A GOOD AROMATHERAPIST?

1. She will display a certificate showing she has been trained at a recognised school. To be an aromatherapist, she will have to be a qualified beauty therapist or a nurse, as she must know a lot about circulation, the nervous system, the lymphatic sysem and skin. Aromatherapy training is very intensive. The aromatherapy massage is completely different to the kind of massage she will have been taught at beauty school.

2. She will reassure you regularly, talk to you about the oils, tell you what she is doing, and generally make you feel relaxed. She will also always make sure you are warm and comfortable. If, at the end of a treatment, you don't feel totally relaxed and almost a little light-headed, the therapist is not the right one for you.

3. She will be clean, with short nails (she wouldn't be able to work properly with long nails), and she must have soft skin. You should never be able to feel her nails or any hard skin.

4. The salon and cubicle will be very clean, and will have tissues covering couches and towels to prevent them becoming oily.

5. She will only use good oils, which do not smell 'off'. If you can only see one or two bottles of oil on her trolley, and she uses just one ready-mixed oil all over the body, you should be dubious. Everyone is different and needs a different combination of oils.

You can tell a good aromatherapist by her knowledge of oils. This is why the consultation is most important.

6. She will offer you home-care advice (see also page 21).

WHAT WILL THE THERAPIST ASK YOU?

1. About yourself: your age; your nationality (the type of skin you have will make a difference to the treatment); your family background (if you have had children, when your skin might be slightly loose on your stomach), etc.

2. About your nervous disposition (some people have skin problems because they are nervous); how you see yourself (whether you are an optimist or a pessimist); whether you get depressed.

3. If you are on any medication (so she can ascertain why you've got a certain condition).

4. About your diet (it may be part of the reason why your skin is clogged up); whether you smoke or drink; what kind of exercise you take; the kind of work you do (and how much you do of it); your hobbies.

5. Whether you are pregnant (if so, she will need to give you a different kind of massage, using only light oils).

6. Whether you have any skin conditions (eg dermatitis, acne, eczema) and how long you've had them; when they flare up etc (you can still have aromatherapy since the oils are antiseptic and won't sting, but the therapist would not massage over broken skin); what your skin condition is like.

7. If you have a heart condition (the therapist would give you a much lighter massage and use lighter oils).

8. About your medical history: operations, accidents, broken bones, spine or back problems (much work is done during the treatment on each side of the spine, working on different zones – by applying pressure on these zones, different organs of the body benefit); serious illnesses, etc; if you are overweight, how long you have been; whether you have high or low blood pressure, irregular or regular periods, digestive problems, circulation problems.

9. If you have had any illnesses (use of a particular oil might make a certain illness recur, so the therapist must know).

WHAT SHOULD YOU ASK THE THERAPIST?
What the treatment will entail, if you've never had it before. Some of the movements might feel strange, so to relax and enjoy them fully you need to know what she is doing to you so that you don't feel tense and can get the full benefit of the treatment.

An Example of a Full Body Aromatherapy Treatment ✍ (NB Different schools teach different methods)

BEFORE
● *Do* have a bath or shower before a treatment as your skin should be clean, with your face free of make-up.
● *Do* make sure you don't feel hungry when you go for a treatment.

- But *don't* have a steam bath, sauna or sunbed directly before a full aromatherapy – you will feel shattered at the end.
- *Don't* have a heavy meal beforehand. Have a light snack.

DURING

1. You'll be asked to undress down to your knickers and to lie down on a couch. You'll be covered with large tissues, a towel and blanket, and the room will probably be darkened, with soothing music playing.

2. The therapist will examine your skin tissue to determine what kind of oils she should use. She may also touch your hands and feet to determine whether you have any circulatory or digestive disorders.

3. She will then decide what kind of massage to give you. If you feel slightly under the weather and the oil is too strong, you might feel sick and dizzy, but a good aromatherapist should recognise the state you are in before she starts work.

4. You will lie on your tummy and the therapist will probably start to relax you by placing her hand on the back of your neck and applying slight pressure with her thumb and finger. Certain pressure points help to relax a client.

5. She will then start to rub in the oil. Don't worry, you won't be smothered in it afterwards – she will only use enough oil to penetrate the skin and give you a proper massage.

One massage technique involves putting pressure on points along both sides of the spine. Each of these pressure points is linked to different organs in the body, and the therapist will be able to see any reactions. She will press each point quite hard – the harder she presses, the better the effect, but it won't be unpleasant.

6. With both hands she will then begin to loosen tissue all over your back, using pleasant rhythmical movements. Then she'll move on to the hip and buttock area, and neck and shoulders.

If you have a lot of tension you might find parts of the massage uncomfortable – as in other kinds of massage – but over a course of treatments the therapist should be able to loosen tension successfully.

7. The difference between aromatherapy and an ordinary massage is that the therapist will be massaging pressure points and working down to the lymph nodes. In addition, oils are much more penetrating than creams, which only sit on the skin, and can be absorbed into the bloodstream.

8. The therapist will massage the back of your legs, and by this time your body will start to feel very relaxed. She may then massage your feet using circular and sliding movements on the soles. She will use a highly antiseptic oil on your feet if they are smelly!

She'll finish this part of the massage by laying her hands on the soles of your feet, which has a wonderful relaxing effect.

9. Now you'll be asked to turn over and you'll be covered with towels and blankets.

10. Since she has just been touching your feet, the aromatherapist will now wash her hands before beginning the next stage of treatment – the face. This can also be a treatment on its own.

11. With her thumb she will softly massage pressure points along the top of your head – from the hairline down to the base of the neck. If she is pressing too hard, tell her! It's not how hard she is doing the movement, but which pressure points she is using. She'll use circular movements on the scalp.

12. She'll now apply a face oil, even if you have oily skin. She might use thyme, bay, rosemary, juniper or niaouli. Don't worry, your face won't be swimming in oil afterwards!

13. She will use a series of different massage movements from the eyebrows to the nose, around the eye area, around the cheeks. Then she'll work down to the neck area, the chest and the neck and shoulders again. All this helps lymphatic drainage: it relieves tension and helps loosen up tissue, which, when it is very tight and clogged, is lacking in elasticity.

The more movements you have, the easier it will be for the oils to penetrate deeper and deeper into the skin. It will also improve the texture of the skin.

14. The therapist might now apply a face mask. She will tissue off excess oil from the face and neck, apply a mask and cover the eyes with pads soaked in some kind of relaxing tonic, such as rosewater or orange blossom. She will make sure your neck and shoulders are covered and that you are warm and comfortable. She will then continue massaging other parts of the body while the mask is working. It takes ten to fifteen minutes.

The mask will depend on your skin condition. If you have acne, for instance, she might use camphor. If you don't like the feeling of a mask that tightens up, tell the therapist in case the one she plans to use will do this. A mask doesn't have to tighten up to be effective!

15. She will now massage the abdomen and solar plexus area (avoiding any recent scars and burns). If she feels there is too much tension in this area, she may make you do a few abdominal exercises – for example, breathing in through the nose and letting the stomach expand, then breathing out through the mouth.

16. She'll now cover the abdomen and expose feet and legs, which she will work on, using sweeping movements from the toes to the top of the legs, and again using pressure points.

HOME COMFORTS

Aromatherapy oils, whether as bath and massage oils or vaporisers, can be used at home to treat all kinds of complaints, from tension to digestive problems. Though they may be expensive, they will last for a very long time since you only need to use a couple of drops at a time.

Ask your therapist to advise you which oils to choose and how to use them.

Your problem	Oils to use
Bad circulation	Geranium, cypress, sage, mugwort, mint, rose, marjoram, basil, cedarwood
Bronchial/lung problems	Eucalyptus, pine, niaouli, thyme, peppermint, camphor, myrrh
Cellulite	Rosemary, pine, juniper, niaouli, geranium, cypress, sage
Cystitis	Sandalwood, juniper, lavender, cypress
Digestive problems	Cardamom, marjoram, parsley, cinnamon, mugwort, peppermint, juniper, orange, verbena
Fluid retention	Juniper, lavender, rosemary, cypress, mugwort, sage, cedarwood
Menopause	Cypress
Period problems	Mugwort, rose, sandalwood, verbena
Sensitive skin	Camomile, thyme (eczema), geranium, neroli, jojoba oil, sandalwood, rose, lemongrass (spots), patchouli (eczema, acne)
Tension	Lavender, juniper, camomile, bergamot, neroli, vetivert (on tummy), thyme, sandalwood

17. She will finish the treatment by laying her hands flat on the soles of your feet for a few seconds.

AFTER
- It's best to rest for an hour afterwards.
- *Don't* use make-up for a day or so, to let oils penetrate.
- You might get a slight reaction, such as red skin, but this will vanish. It's most unlikely you will be allergic to any of the oils, but if you get a reaction that doesn't go away after a day or so, you should go back to the aromatherapist for her advice.
- Your hair will look awful, so don't plan to go out somewhere special directly afterwards. Obviously, there's no point, either, in turning up for a treatment with freshly washed hair.

RESULTS

You should feel wonderfully relaxed, and your skin should be gleaming. And, I'm told, some of the oils used work as aphrodisiacs!

You should enjoy the effects for at least 24 hours. The more often you can afford to have treatments, and the more used to them you become, the more benefits you'll derive.

ADDITIONAL FACTS

● If you hate the smell of any oil, say so. Some oils smell very strongly, and all will linger, some longer than others. Rose, for example, which is good for improving circulation, is particularly strong and can make you feel a bit sick if you don't like it.

● An aromatherapist should be able to make up individual oils for clients, incorporating different kinds with properties you need.

● A therapist might encourage the oils to penetrate by using very hot compresses, aromatic baths, warming lamps, and other forms of massage.

Further Information ✍

Most qualified aromatherapists will be listed with the Federation of Aromatherapists or the Association of Aromatherapists. BABTAC (see details on page 11) will also be able to recommend a therapist. Send a large s.a.e. with your enquiry.

The International Federation of Aromatherapists, 46 Dalkeith Road, West Dulwich, London SE21 8LS.

The Association of Aromatherapists, 44 Ditchling Rise, Brighton, Sussex BN1 4QN.

There are also many books available on aromatherapy. Some of the best are:

Alternative Medicine by Andrew Stanway (Macdonald)
Practical Aromatherapy by Shirley Price (Thorsons)
The Art of Aromatherapy by Robert Tisserand (C. W. Daniel)
The Aromatherapy Handbook by Danièle Ryman (Century)
The Practice of Aromatherapy by Dr Jean Valnet (C. W. Daniel)

MAN APPEAL? **Yes.**	PLEASURE RATING **+5**

BLEACHING

The Facts

WHAT IS IT?

Bleaching is a temporary way of camouflaging superfluous hair growth by lightening the hair to blend in with your skin tone. It is ideal if you prefer not to remove the actual hair, for whatever reason.

You can use bleach on any part of the body – upper lip, chin, arms, eyebrows, legs – though the therapist will use different bleach solutions on different parts of the body.

You can, of course, buy ready-made bleach solutions from your chemist if you want to bleach your own hair at home: if you do this, you must follow the instructions very carefully. The advantage of having it done in the salon is that the therapist can assess your hair and skin type, and will be able to mix the right solution for you.

WHERE CAN YOU HAVE IT DONE?

- At beauty salons
- At health farms and clubs
- At some hairdressers
- On board ships, etc (anywhere with a trained beauty therapist)

HOW MUCH SHOULD IT COST?

It depends on the area you want to have treated. Expect to pay from £5 for upper lip and from £8 for legs.

HOW OFTEN SHOULD YOU HAVE IT?

Normally, every three to six weeks, depending on the area being treated. Everyone is different.

Never overdo it, as (a) you could bleach hair so white it would look unnatural; (b) you could burn the skin slightly; and (c) if you leave the bleach on for too long you could bleach the skin.

Remember, you can only bleach hair to blonde. If you simply want to go a lighter colour on the eyebrows (say, you've dyed your hair from black to light brown and want your eyebrows to match) you would need a tint (see Lash and Brow tinting, page 93).

HOW LONG SHOULD IT TAKE?

Again, this depends on the hair being treated; it could take anything from three to ten minutes. For example, if you have light brown hair, you'd only need the bleach on upper lip hair for three to four minutes. Allow fifteen minutes for a visit to the salon.

DO TRY BLEACHING:

1. if you are self-conscious about superfluous hair but do not want to resort to other methods of removal.
2. if you have a slight down on the arms and legs that would be difficult to remove.
3. if you've had your hair bleached and want your eyebrows to match, to make it look more natural. Eyebrow hair doesn't grow like the hair on your head, so you don't need to worry about black roots appearing. The bleached colour will simply fade out.
4. if you are older, or have been unwell, and can't face the discomfort associated with other forms of hair removal.

DON'T TRY BLEACHING:

1. if you have very sensitive skin.
2. if you are prone to allergies.
3. if you have any skin problems, eg eczema or psoriasis.

WHAT WILL THE THERAPIST ASK YOU?

1. If you have any allergies, and to what. You may be allergic to certain skin products, tints and dyes. If she feels that your skin could be sensitive she might give you a free patch test behind the ear beforehand. You'd go back for treatment 24 hours later.
2. If you've ever used any bleach before. If you've been using bleach at home and have damaged the skin or hair, she'll recom-

mend that you leave the skin to return to normal before she attempts to bleach the area again.

A Typical
Bleaching Session on the Upper Lip ✐

BEFORE
● You should not be wearing any make-up, but the therapist will clean your skin anyway.

DURING
1. The therapist will cover your shoulders and clothing to avoid spillage, then ask you to lie on your back on the couch.
2. She will first clean the area with a cleansing cream, then a little tonic lotion, to make sure all grease has been removed.
3. Depending on the texture and colour of the hair, she will mix up the appropriate bleach solution, which is a mixture of ammonia and bicarbonate of soda. It will either be applied with a little spatula or a brush. The smell won't be particularly strong.
4. She will check that you don't feel any burning, and then she will leave the solution on your hair for the correct length of time.
5. Some hair reacts quicker to bleach than others, so if it's your first visit to the salon the therapist may take the bleach off after a couple of minutes to check on the progress. If you're not bleached yet, she will reapply it.
6. When the treatment is complete she will remove the bleach with damp cotton wool or a wet sponge. The area will be dried with tissues, and a soothing cream such as Savlon applied.

AFTER
● *Don't* apply make-up to the area for at least 24 hours.
● If you have a treatment on your arms or legs, it's best not to have a hot bath afterwards, or a steam treatment.

RESULTS
Hair should be bleached blonde and natural looking to blend in with the skin tone.

ADDITIONAL FACTS
● If the solution is left on for too long or is too strong it could burn

your skin. You should only ever experience a slight tingling sensation so if you feel any burning at any time, tell the therapist *immediately* to avoid any damage.

• If you have any burns – *sue the salon!* The therapist has been negligent.

Home Care ✍

If you feel a burning sensation before the recommended time on a home kit, take it off immediately and apply an antiseptic cream, such as Savlon, to the area.

Incidentally, if you overdo the bleaching with home treatments you could make the hair coarser.

MAN APPEAL?	
Possibly for eyebrows	PLEASURE RATING −1

BUST TREATMENTS

The Facts

WHAT ARE THEY?

More and more British women these days take care of their faces, their hair, their hands and their feet, but they don't give a thought to their breasts until they notice they're not at their peak (if you excuse the expression!). And by then the damage has been done.

Continental women have been having bust treatments as often as they would a facial, and beauty therapists here believe that regular treatment can prevent stretch marks and keep the bust firm and supple. As a result, most of the French beauty houses in the UK – Clarins, DeCleor, René Guinot and G. M. Collin (see also Cathiodermie page 34) – offer bust treatments.

In this country therapists say women are not yet used to the idea of having their bust treated. They are usually inhibited, and feel it's not quite the thing to do, or that it's too late for them, or that therapists cannot do anything for the bust. Many haven't even heard that they can have their bust treated, and that there are products on the market which could help improve the condition of the bust.

But bust treatments are now being gradually introduced into salons, and more and more women are asking about them. A good therapist, noticing during a facial that her client has crepey skin on the breast area, may recommend a series of bust treatments. Your skin doesn't stop under the chin!

If you see a salon advertising bust treatments you should get unbiased advice. The therapist should sit you down and tell you what – if anything – a series of bust treatments can do for you.

If your breast has dropped quite dramatically, no amount of treatment will put it back to the way it was when you were twenty. But, say therapists, bust treatment can improve the skin tone and make the skin look smoother and less wrinkled.

WHERE CAN YOU TRY ONE?
- At beauty salons in around 90 countries
- At health farms – where people tend to chat about their treatments and can encourage you to try one which you might not otherwise try

WHEN SHOULD YOU HAVE ONE?
Bust treatments are best used as a preventative measure, and when you start having them should depend on when you start developing. In your teens, for example, simply using a good bust product regularly at home could help strengthen tissue.

But don't expect miracles – if you've got 100 per cent sag, there's nothing you can do!

HOW MUCH SHOULD IT COST?
Treatments are usually priced individually, although you'll need a course (see below). You often pay for eleven and get one free if you pay in advance. A Clarins bust treatment (see page 31) can cost anything from £80 to £130 for a course, which works out at around £8 to £10 a treatment.

But it may be that you only need to use one product at home to keep your bust in good condition, so it's worth getting a therapist to assess what kind of treatment you need rather than simply demanding a series of treatments.

HOW OFTEN SHOULD YOU HAVE ONE?
- A one-off treatment will be a waste of time. You'll need to have a course of treatments, ideally once a year as a preventative measure. A course should involve two treatments a week for six weeks if your bust is in good condition, though a therapist may feel you don't need treatment and may simply advise you to use products at home to keep your skin in good, firm order.
- If you are beginning to see signs of ageing and want to firm and lift the bust, it would be advisable to have a course of treatments and then use home products for maintenance.

But remember, you're not going to see a dramatic change in the size of your bust!

BUST DO'S AND DONT'S

DO:

- remember always to pull the shoulders back when sitting or standing. It will lift the breast. Never slouch!
- try these simple exercises to help lift the breast into position:

  1. Say 'Eeks, oh', stretching your jaw as far as possible. It will pull on all the muscles, working on the natural 'strap' which runs from the nipple up to the shoulders.

  2. Cross your arms in front of you and imagine you are pulling up your sleeves.

- go swimming regularly. Swimming will keep your shoulders loose and help your deportment. It will also pull your bust back. Other good exercises for the bust include 'praying' – pressing your palms together – and standing in doorways with your hands on the doorposts and pushing outwards. All these exercises work on the pectoral muscles.

  Exercises which strengthen the spine are also beneficial. One exercise they do in France is to swing on a doorframe – simply lift your legs off the floor!

- use a suntan lotion with a high protection factor if you're thinking of sunbathing topless. Use a higher factor than you use on the rest of the body because the nipple area isn't usually exposed to the elements and you can easily burn.

DON'T:

- spray perfume across the décolleté. Perfume can damage the connective tissue.
- soak in hot baths. Cold water firms the bust, so if you like your baths hot, cool off afterwards by splashing on cold water to tighten the tissues sufficiently and keep them in position. Always moisturise afterwards.
- breastfeed your babies for more than three to four months if you want to keep your bust in good condition. After that time, you will be drawing off the fat cells in the bust, which tends to decrease the volume.
- wear a bra that's too tight under your bust. You'll get a line there, and also your bra will be cutting off the circulation to your breast. Never wear a bra with too-tight shoulder straps because you'll get deep indentations in your shoulders as well as having your breast pushed out of its natural position.

  Every time you buy a bra, you should go to a specialist who will measure you correctly. A good bra should fit like a glove and be so comfortable that you're not even aware of it. Bear in mind that we all expand and contract premenstrually and with weight loss and gain. So a bra that fitted you last month might not be right for you now.

  Avoid padded bras, which act as a heat trap and make the bust perspire. Cotton bras are best.

HOW LONG SHOULD A TREATMENT TAKE?

It will take 30 to 45 minutes. The first treatment may take a little longer because the therapist will first spend time assessing your needs, measuring your bust, and giving you general advice on diet, etc.

DO TRY A BUST TREATMENT:

1. if you want to keep your bust in good shape.
2. at the beginning of a pregnancy. Your bust will increase quite dramatically when you are pregnant, causing a great deal of strain on the skin. If you have bust treatment early on to get the skin in good condition, your skin should be able to cope with the strain as you get larger.

You shouldn't be too tender to try a treatment during the first few months of pregnancy, and the treatments are very gentle. Besides, now is the time to ask your therapist's advice about the kind of products you should be using on your breasts during pregnancy to help minimise any unpleasant after-effects such as stretch marks and sagging.

3. if you have premenstrual tension, which causes a build-up in the lymphatic system, making the bust very swollen and tender. A bust treatment – which involves very gentle massage – can relieve a lot of the pressure and drain the bust of any build-up.
4. if you're about to go on holiday. A series of bust treatments will make your skin much smoother and healthier looking. And you should get a more even tan, too.

DON'T TRY A BUST TREATMENT:

1. if your breasts are very tender, due to mastitis, for example.
2. if you have any medical condition.
3. if you have any suspicious lumps.
4. if, when you lean forward and let your bust droop, you can put one hand above the bust and one underneath and make your hands touch through the skin. That means that the tissue has completely deteriorated, and you'll be wasting your money.

HOW CAN YOU TELL A GOOD THERAPIST?

1. A good therapist will be a sounding board for all your problems. Unlike a doctor, who doesn't have time to take an interest in a woman's aesthetic beauty, a therapist will be ready to listen and offer advice.

You can't go to a doctor and say 'Doctor, my bust is sagging'. He'll say it's your age, and you can't do anything about it. A good therapist will make you feel good about yourself.

2. It's a good idea to feel comfortable with the therapist. If you're going to a new salon, it's best to try out the salon first. Perhaps opt for a manicure or pedicure, then a body treatment or facial so that you get used to the therapist's touch.

When you feel comfortable with her, you could then ask if she does any bust treatments, and whether she could give you advice. That way, you can also assess her knowledge and ability as she should be able to tell you what you can realistically expect from treatments.

3. A few salons now include a bust treatment with a facial, which is a good way of eliminating the initial stress of having a bust treatment. The therapist may work over the breast – albeit very briefly – during a facial massage.

A good therapist will let you know in advance that she's going to do this and why, so that you get the chance to refuse this part of the treatment if you want.

4. She will display her qualifications on the wall of the salon. These will usually include a certificate from the company with whose products she is working.

An Example of a Clarins Bust Treatment ✑

(NB each company has its own methods and products; Clarins' products include a range of bust milks and tonic lotions for all skin types.)

BEFORE
● You'll be asked to undress down to your slip and pants, and be given a robe to wear while the therapist finds out about your medical history and your needs. She may then show you some exercises which you should do at home.
● If the therapist plans to incorporate some electrical treatment during the session, she will check that you don't have a pacemaker or metal plates which might be affected by the electricity (see Slendertone, page 138).
● The therapist will ask whether you want to develop, reduce or simply maintain your shape.

DURING
1. You'll be asked to lie down on your back, and you will be covered with a towel. The first treatment is always the worst,

because you don't know what to expect, so the therapist should use this time to explain what she's going to do.

Many people worry about having a bust treatment – they think it's a bit 'funny' having someone massage their bust. But it doesn't feel as you'd expect. It is simply like a continuation of a facial.

2. The therapist will then cleanse the breast area, using a cleanser and cotton wool pads in a soothing outward rhythm. She will cleanse right up to the chin.

Her movements should be light, not heavy. A bust treatment can be very relaxing because the breast area – particularly down the sternum – is a tension point, which can only benefit from light massage.

3. She will then apply the appropriate bust milk in a series of movements, all of which work on the fat content of the bust. There are milks which firm and strengthen, which develop and firm, or which reduce, depending on your wishes.

She will lightly massage around the bust area, using a cupping movement which lifts and drains the breast at the same time. Her top hand will go down towards the armpit, which is a lymphatic drainage area. This movement also helps to improve circulation.

The bust milk acts rather like the cups of your bra, containing the bust by working on the tissue holding your breast in position. If that tissue starts to go, your bust will start to drop, which is why it's so important to work on this area.

4. Now it's time to work on the 'straps' which are holding up your cups. The therapist will use a concentrated essence – an 'ampoule' – which is strengthening, firming and tightening. It's made from a mixture of tissue and plant extracts.

She will work this in along the area from the nipple to the chin, which is the body's natural 'bra strap'.

5. She will finish off by applying a bust tonic, which 'fixes' the treatment. This will be quite cold – unlike the rest of the treatment – and coldness on the bust causes it to contract, just as if you were running in and out of the sea!

AFTER
- You should feel pleasantly relaxed.
- Your skin should be smooth and silky.

RESULTS
The effects of the treatment should last one or two days, and after a course of treatment you should notice an improvement in the shape and appearance of your bust.

Home Care ✍

A therapist will usually advise you to moisturise the bust area and keep the skin in good condition – especially if you're pregnant, or losing or gaining weight very quickly for whatever reason (illness, stress, or just plain dieting), when the skin is under more pressure.

Remember that the skin is like a giant piece of elastic which is expanding and contracting, and over the years it won't go back. That's why the therapist should advise you which treatment to have, and what treatment you should be doing at home, particularly when you are more stressed.

You'll be told to avoid hot baths, too-tight bras, and advised to eat sensibly and do regular light exercises. You might even want to buy a machine that you can attach to the cold water tap so that you can massage the bust every day with cold water.

Further Information ✍

The following companies will all be able to recommend local salons offering bust treatments using their products:

Clarins, 4 Queen Street, Mayfair, London W1. Tel: 01–629 2979.

DeCleor (UK) Ltd, 58 Paddington Street, London W1M 3RR. Tel: 01–486 3957.

(René Guinot), R. Robson Ltd, Dept GH6, Ensign House, Queens Road, Sunninghill, Berks. SL5 9AQ. Tel: Ascot (0990) 26133.

G. M. Collin, Beeston Grange, Sandy, Beds. SG19 1PG. Tel: Sandy (0767) 82288.

CATHIODERMIE

The Facts

WHAT IS IT?

Cathiodermie is a treatment that is said to 'simultaneously rehydrate, rejuvenate and deep cleanse the skin' using electric currents.

Devised by a French cosmetic chemist, René Guinot (who also made his own products to reinforce the treatment), it has been available in France for around 30 years and in England for over 15. René Guinot discovered that the extracts of sea plants, herbs, fruit and flowers used on the skin in conjunction with certain electric currents could improve skin texture and treat difficult skin conditions such as acne.

Cathiodermie treatments include:

a) a facial, described here.

b) an eye treatment which helps reduce the surrounding fine lines. It takes about an hour and includes a special massage. If you have particularly sensitive eyes the therapist would do a test patch first.

c) a neck treatment.

d) a firming bust treatment (see Bust Treatments, page 27).

WHERE CAN YOU TRY IT?

● In over 800 beauty salons in France, and 2,500 salons throughout the world; in some countries it is called Hydradermie

● At Steiner Beauty Rooms

● At most health farms

● On board many ships

HOW MUCH SHOULD A CATHIODERMIE FACIAL COST?

The average price is £15, though expect to pay more in London. You're paying for an hour and a half of a beauty therapist's time, and the products are very expensive.

HOW OFTEN SHOULD YOU HAVE ONE?

- Ideally, once a month, which is the normal cycle of the skin. For an oily skin, once a fortnight.
- For young skin with acne, once a week for three weeks, then once a fortnight for a further three treatments.
- For eye, neck and bust treatments, two treatments a week for six to eight weeks.

HOW LONG DOES A CATHIODERMIE FACIAL TAKE?

Between one and a quarter and one and a half hours. If the treatment lasts less than an hour and a quarter, the therapist is not giving you a full treatment.

The French like to standardise everything, and during the treatment many of the stages last seven minutes. Whether you have a Cathiodermie in Putney or Hong Kong, it should be a standard treatment, and any claims that clients aren't receiving standard Cathiodermie treatment will be investigated.

DO TRY CATHIODERMIE:

1. if you want a good, deep-cleansing facial. It's also a very pleasant and relaxing treatment.
2. if you have acne.

DON'T TRY CATHIODERMIE:

1. if you have metal plates or a pacemaker. Cathiodermie uses an electric current which could affect these.
2. if you have epilepsy – again, because of the electric current.
3. if you're under the age of fifteen, unless your therapist is working in conjunction with a skin specialist to cure acne. Quite often a teenage skin will improve itself by the age of sixteen or seventeen.
4. if you're newly pregnant, especially if it's your first treatment and you're nervous. Although Cathiodermie is quite safe, if anything were to go wrong with your pregnancy, you might blame it on the treatment.
5. if you're in the last stages of pregnancy. It will be too uncomfortable to lie down for an hour and a half.

6. if you've just had a course of electrical treatments of any kind, eg electrolysis.

7. if you've just had facial waxing, a sauna or been on a sunbed. You need to allow three to four hours before having a Cathiodermie after any of these treatments. You'll also have to allow three to four hours *after* having a Cathiodermie before having one of them.

8. if you've just come out of a Jacuzzi. The chemicals used in a Jacuzzi could react with the treatment and cause an allergy.

HOW CAN YOU TELL IF A THERAPIST IS TRAINED?

René Guinot hold four-day training courses in Sunningale for qualified beauty therapists. Once trained, therapists are given their own personal certificate which they will take with them from salon to salon.

If there's no certificate on display in a salon offering Cathiodermie, it could be because the therapist has been taught by a friend or colleague. There shouldn't be any danger in going to an unqualified therapist, but you won't necessarily get the same quality of treatment.

A Typical Cathiodermie Facial Treatment ✍

BEFORE
- You'll need to remove all your jewellery.
- You shouldn't be wearing any make-up. If you are, the therapist will have to remove it before starting the treatment.

DURING
1. You will be asked to undress and lie on a tissue-covered couch. You'll need to remove your top so that the therapist can work on the neck area, but you can keep your bra on if you like – the straps will be pulled down though. Since you'll be in the same position for quite some time, it's also a good idea to remove your skirt or trousers for comfort and to avoid creasing.

You'll then be well covered in towels, with only your face and shoulders exposed.

2. The therapist will thoroughly cleanse and tone your skin, then blot it to make sure she's removed every trace of grease from your face.

3. She'll apply a solution called Electro Z, which contains trace elements. These speed up the metabolism and will help reduce the skin's natural resistance to the electrical current.

4. She'll then apply a Cathiodermie gel, specially formulated for your particular skin type.

● *If you have dry/normal skin*, she'll use a soothing and emollient gel containing orange blossom, arnica, quinquina bark, nettle, birch and camomile.

● *If you have greasy skin*, she'll use a soothing and emollient gel containing sulphurated amino-acids which help to check the production of sebum. This contains nettle, cress, birch, guaiacum wood, yeast, melissa and camphor.

● *If you have dry, wrinkle-prone skin*, she'll choose an anti-sag, anti-wrinkle gel containing elastin, collagen, mucopoly-saccharides and tissue extract.

GELS USED IN CATHIODERMIE

Gel contents	Properties
Orange blossom	Soothing
Arnica	Stimulating
Nettle	Astringent, tonic
Quinquina bark	Astringent, tonic
Camomile	Anti-inflammatory, tonic
Birch	Astringent, tonic
Cress	Decongesting
Guaiacum wood	Anti-inflammatory, soothing
Yeast	Purifying, lightening
Melissa	Revitalising, stimulating
Camphor	Soothing, antiseptic
Elastin	Elasticity, revitalising
Collagen	Suppleness, hydrating, revitalising
Mucopolysaccharides	Hydrating
Tissue extract	Stimulating

These gels also contain three elements – sodium lactate, acid sodium carbonate, and trace elements – which have different reactions, all happening simultaneously:

● *Sodium lactate* causes an osmotic tension in the skin. Basically, this means that it encourages the body's own processes to draw fluid from the saline of the blood and therefore rehydrate the skin.

● *Acid sodium carbonate* changes from an acid into an alkali. In the skin we have toxins and sebum that together form a fatty acid. When this fatty acid meets the alkali it saponifies – that is, it forms a soap. This soap is pushed on to the surface of the skin by the body's own natural processes, such as perspiration, and is the deep-cleansing factor of the treatment.

● *Trace elements* are the catalysts which speed up the whole process of cell renewal.

5. Once the gels are on the skin, the current can be applied to activate the components within the gels. You'll be given the correct amount of current for your skin type.

The negative electrode is a small metal rod and you'll be asked to hold it in your hand. The therapist will then use the rollers – which are positive – to help push the gel into the skin.

She will first do a test to check that the setting she chooses for you produces the correct reading on your skin. Then she'll start. You won't feel anything except the rollers going over your face!

There's a set sequence of strokes, which starts on the neck, moves under and over the chin, then works up the face. The aim is to work over the whole area of the face, except the eyes. The gel is quite cooling and pleasant.

6. The therapist will then reapply gel wherever needed, and use the fork electrode (a two-pronged fork with bobbles at the end) for seven minutes, going up and down the nose to start with, then getting into all the nooks and crannies you can't get to with rollers – around the nostril area, for example.

7. She'll now disconnect the machine and remove gel from the centre of the face and from any other area where she plans to extract commedones – the beauty therapists' term for blackheads!

This is the worst bit of the facial. The therapist will squeeze blocked pores with tissues wrapped around her fingers, to open up the pores. Ouch! It is, however, the most important part of the treatment, and one that the therapist mustn't cut down on.

8. The next stage involves applying a stabilised, oxygenated cream and using a high-frequency current to cause it to become unstable. In other words, the oxygen will mix with free atoms and become ozone, which has a bactericidal effect. This is where the skin is warmed and the growth of new cells boosted – and it's ideal for acne.

After applying the cream, she will cover your face with a dry gauze square. If you're claustrophobic she can cut small holes in it. This creates a gap between the skin and the high frequency, which helps it create ozone more quickly. She'll plug in the high frequency handset, attach a Perspex bulb and set the timer to seven minutes. You'll hear a zizzing noise and feel a slight tingle as it's rubbed over your skin, but it's not unpleasant.

This high frequency current is an alternating current which oscillates, and it can be used as a treatment by itself. If a therapist has just extracted some spots, she can 'spark' them, to dry them up.

She'll now remove any excess cream with damp cotton wool, and your skin will be toned.

9. It's now massage time – the most relaxing part of the treatment. If you're a little tense about having electrical treatment, this will certainly relax your back and shoulders. Without a massage, Cathiodermie would be a rather impersonal treatment. The beauty therapist will bring in her own technique of relaxing massage.

10. She will now apply a specially-prepared face mask all over the face, neck and décolleté. It will be pleasant and cooling and it won't set. She'll place some pads over your eyes and leave you to relax for ten minutes.

11. The mask is removed with a spatula and your face is then toned and moisturised. It's important to make sure the skin is perfectly clean after the treatment, and that all the gel has been removed.

AFTER

● Your skin might become a bit spotty, as all the impurities have been brought to the surface. It is best to have your treatment at least a week before a special occasion.

● You shouldn't wear make-up for at least six hours, though you can obviously wear lipstick and eye make-up immediately after a Cathiodermie facial. After an eye treatment, allow three hours before using eye make-up.

● Your hair will look a mess, having been covered for so long and oiled around the hairline, and your face may look rather shiny, so don't plan to go straight to an important date!

RESULTS

Three or four days after a Cathiodermie, your skin should look wonderful. Some people's skin glows immediately afterwards, though others can look pale or ruddy, or even slightly blotchy, although this should fade after a couple of hours.

Home Care ✒

Your therapist should advise you on products to use between treatments.

Further Information ✒

The sole distributors for Laboratoires René Guinot in the UK, Republic of Ireland, Australia, New Zealand and Bermuda are:

R. Robson Ltd, Dept GH6, Ensign House, Queens Road, Sunninghill, Berks. SL5 9AQ. Tel: Ascot (0990) 26133.

If you ring them, they will recommend salons in your area. Alternatively, if you write you'll be sent a leaflet, a free sample of one of their products, and the name, address and telephone number of your nearest salon.

MAN APPEAL? **Yes**	PLEASURE RATING **+3**

CLEORTHERM

The Facts

WHAT IS IT?

Cleortherm is a kind of heat treatment for the whole body, except the face, which is particularly good for cellulite and improving circulation. First you'll be covered in essential oils and gels, then you'll be wrapped in a specially adapted and insulated electric blanket, and left to 'sweat it out'.

Heat treatments, such as saunas and steam baths, are often used to reinforce the effects of treatments which use electric currents (Slendertone, for instance) as part of a slimming treatment, though salons with limited space may offer Cleortherm in place of other heat treatments.

Cleortherm is suitable for all ages and is quite safe. The blankets are waterproof and insulated so there's absolutely no chance of getting an electric shock.

WHERE CAN YOU TRY IT?

- In some salons
- At most health farms
- On certain cruise ships

HOW MUCH SHOULD IT COST?

Anywhere between £15 and £30 per treatment. On average, expect to pay around £20.

HOW OFTEN SHOULD YOU HAVE IT?

● Once or twice a week at a salon, or up to three times a week at a health farm where you are under daily supervision. You should benefit most from a course of treatments, so don't expect a dramatic result after just one treatment.

● If you have a small amount of cellulite, you will need around six treatments; for hard, dimpling cellulite expect to have up to twenty treatments. A therapist might recommend Cleortherm along with other treatments such as G5 (see page 73).

● You can overdo this treatment – not because of the products involved but because overheating the body can actually make it sag (and you need to be particularly careful about heating your bust). So if the therapist advises only one treatment a week for six weeks, take her advice!

HOW LONG SHOULD A TREATMENT TAKE?

About 30 to 45 minutes. It's a fairly boring treatment, so it's worth asking the therapist if you can have a manicure or pedicure at the same time.

DO TRY A CLEORTHERM:

1. if you suffer from fluid retention, especially on the tops of your legs, on the bottom or tummy, or if you have puffy ankles or feet. After one treatment you should notice both weight and inch loss since up to 4½ lb (2 kg) of body fluids are eliminated during treatment.
2. if you want to firm up flabby tops of legs or thighs.
3. if you are trying to get rid of cellulite – the condition which gives the skin an orange-peel appearance when squeezed between the fingers.
4. if you suffer from poor circulation. Incidentally, women with bad circulation are more susceptible to cellulite.
5. if you have rheumatoid or muscular fibrosis, or any muscular condition.
6. if you suffer from tension.

DON'T TRY A CLEORTHERM:

1. if you suffer from diabetes.
2. if you are pregnant.
3. if you have any heart condition.
4. if you have high or low blood pressure.
5. if you have varicose veins.

6. if you suffer from claustrophobia because, with the exception of your head, you're going to be totally enclosed, with your arms down by your sides.

7. if you suffer from epilepsy.

8. if you have any cuts or bruises, or have recently had an operation.

9. if you are on any medication.

HOW CAN YOU TELL IF A THERAPIST IS GOOD?

1. A Cleortherm will always be given by a qualified beauty therapist, and the manufacturers, DeCleor, run courses on the application of their products.

2. A therapist should stay with you throughout the treatment in case you begin to feel uncomfortable or want any other assistance. She will make sure you have sufficient pillows under your head, and she should also have a damp flannel on hand to mop your brow – you will appreciate this!

FIGHT CELLULITE WITH DIET

If you want to lose weight or banish cellulite, heat treatments, massage and exercise alone won't do the trick. You *must* combine treatments with *diet*! Your therapist should be able to advise you on a suitable course of action.

Certain foods – such as salty and smoked foods, sugar and white flour – are thought to contribute to the formation of cellulite, as are diuretic drinks (strange as it may seem) such as alcohol, tea and coffee. So keep the following list of 'foods to avoid' by your fridge:

alcohol	cream	pastries
anchovies	coffee	pizza
avocados	frankfurters	potato salad
bacon	gravy	peanut butter
blue cheese	mayonnaise	salami
bananas	milk shakes	salted crackers
corned beef	macaroni	salted nuts
carbonated drinks	olives	soured cream
chili con carne	pickles	spaghetti in sauce
chips	pork	tabasco
chocolate	popcorn	tea

DO, however, eat lots of green vegetables!

A Typical Cleortherm Treatment ✍

BEFORE
- If possible, have a hot shower, which will improve your circulation.
- Have a drink of water.
- Make sure you have no oils already on your body.
- Never have a massage directly before a treatment.
- *Don't* have a large meal directly before, because the heat might make you feel sick.
- Though it won't do you any harm, it might be best to avoid going on a sunbed directly before a treatment as it will heat up your body and may make the Cleortherm treatment rather uncomfortable.

DURING
1. You'll be asked to undress completely and to lie on your front on the couch. It's a good idea to ask the therapist if you can keep your pants on to stop your backside becoming too uncomfortable during the treatment.

   The couch will be covered first in an ordinary blanket, then with a towel, then the thermal blanket, and finally a plastic sheet (which is part of the treatment as it acts as an insulator). You'll lie on top of this lot.

2. Starting with the soles of the feet and ending with the palms of the hands (hands are the most porous part of your body), the therapist will then massage in a small amount of diuretic oil – not too much, otherwise it will act as an insulator. She'll then apply a gel which will act on the circulation and tone the skin, then ask you to turn over so she can apply the oil and gel to the front of your body.

3. You'll then be 'wrapped up' from neck to toe in the uppermost layer of plastic sheeting, which will protect the thermal blanket and towels from the gel on the surface of the skin. You may feel a tingling sensation as the oil and gels start to work.

4. You'll now be wrapped firmly in the towel and blanket combination described above, which will be fastened with Velcro. For comfort, and to keep all the heat in, a towel will be placed around your neck. You will look rather like an Egyptian mummy, and feel as if you're lying tucked up snugly in a narrow bed and have just realised you've forgotten to turn off the electric blanket!

5. Now you'll be left to sweat for up to 45 minutes, possibly helped by overhead heat lamps. It's not the most interesting or

comfortable of treatments as you will have to stay in exactly the same position for the duration of the treatment.

It's worth bearing in mind that the more regularly you exercise and the better your circulation, the quicker you'll start to perspire.

6. The therapist should check at regular intervals that you are comfortable, and mop your brow – or perhaps apply a pleasant-smelling, cooling spray to the face – from time to time.

7. At the end of the treatment, you'll be unwrapped, and towelled down to remove perspiration. The therapist will then apply a tonic lotion so that you do not feel cold, and finally she may apply a body oil.

AFTER

- *Don't* have a shower for the rest of the day as the oils will still be working at cellular level for several hours after the treatment.
- *Don't* immediately have a large meal – you might feel sick.
- *Do* have a massage (manual or G5) or Slendertone treatment.
- You might feel a bit 'woozy' – that's due to the heating of the body. So it's best to do something restful or to lie down for half an hour. Avoid anything energetic, such as swimming or a dance class (you wouldn't feel much like it anyway).
- You'll be very thirsty. Though you may be reluctant to drink afterwards in case you replace the fluid you've just lost, a glass or two of water may, in fact, help the diuretics to work, eliminating the toxins and impurities from your system.
- You will be literally dripping when you're unwrapped – as will your knickers. (They will feel a bit 'tacky' but this washes out very easily.)
- Your hair will probably be rather messy, so don't expect to go somewhere special immediately after a treatment.

RESULTS

You should feel very relaxed, and there may be a diuretic effect which will last for a few days. Your skin should also feel soft and supple.

If you measure yourself directly after a treatment you won't necessarily notice a reduction in your size because when you heat your body you sometimes puff up temporarily (you've probably noticed how tight your shoes are just after a hot bath).

You may, however, be slightly lighter – though the full effects will only be felt after the diuretic oils have been at work for a while, draining the body of excess fluid (ie, making you go to the loo!).

Home Care 🖋

The therapist should be able to advise you on products to use at home in conjunction with a controlled anti-cellulite or slimming diet.

Further Information 🖋

Only pure aromatherapy oils and natural plant ingredients are used in this treatment.

If you want to find out where you can obtain a Cleortherm treatment, contact:

DeCleor (UK) Ltd, 58 Paddington Street, London W1M 3RR. Tel: 01–486 3957.

MAN APPEAL? **Yes**	PLEASURE RATING **−3**

Collagen Facial

The Facts

WHAT IS IT?
A collagen facial is a rejuvenating facial most suitable for older skins, and may reduce signs of ageing such as fine lines.

Collagen is the protein in the skin, which we begin to lose as we get older. Once it has gone completely, there's nothing you can do about it, but a collagen facial should help to strengthen the existing fibres and to slow down their degeneration.

Collagen made its appearance in the beauty world only recently. It had previously been used by French doctors to treat burns and wounds. They had discovered that sheets made from collagen (from the muscle fibre of young cattle) were very healing and helped to restore damaged fibres.

You can't have collagen injections in a beauty salon – that can only be done by a doctor. The collagen masks applied in salons do not go into the bloodstream.

WHERE CAN YOU TRY IT?
- At beauty salons
- At health farms and possibly certain health clubs

HOW MUCH SHOULD IT COST?
Approximately £35 to £40.

HOW OFTEN SHOULD YOU HAVE ONE?
Ideally, you should have a course of six treatments twice a year to get the full benefit.

HOW LONG SHOULD A TREATMENT TAKE?
Between 45 and 60 minutes.

DO TRY A COLLAGEN FACIAL:
1. if you're over 25 and are developing fine lines. Reassuringly, the more lines you have, the more visible the results, say therapists.
2. if you're about to go on holiday to a hot climate – it's an ideal preventative treatment.
3. if you're getting married the next day – even one treatment will give your skin a wonderful, healthy glow.

DON'T TRY A COLLAGEN FACIAL:
1. if you're under 25. It's a rather expensive facial which you are unlikely to need at your age. It's more sensible to have a facial more suited to your skin type (see Facials, page 65).
2. if you have developed an allergy in the past to collagen creams. Very few people are allergic to collagen protein, however, and, incidentally, if you *do* develop an allergy, it will go within a few days.

HOW CAN YOU TELL A GOOD THERAPIST?
In the hands of a qualified beauty therapist, there's little that can go wrong in this simple treatment.

But the sign of a good therapist, as always, is someone with a pleasing touch, someone who gives you a good massage, stays with you throughout the treatment, and continually checks that you are warm and comfortable.

WHAT SHOULD THE THERAPIST ASK YOU?
1. If you have had any reaction to any beauty products (which might contain collagen).
2. Whether you are allergic to certain foods, such as meat. If in doubt, a therapist would give you a collagen sample to take home to test for a reaction behind your ear before having a full facial.

A Typical Thalgo Collagen Facial ✐

BEFORE
- *Don't* wear any make-up as the therapist will need to take it off.
- Remove contact lenses and earrings.

DURING

1. You'll be asked to undress down to your underwear. If you want to keep your bra on the therapist will need to push down your bra straps so she can work on the shoulder area. You'll then lie on your back on a couch, and will be covered with towels. Your hair will be tied back.

2. The therapist will start by cleansing your face, removing any traces of grime and make-up. She will then apply a toning lotion.

3. The next stage involves preparing the skin by applying a mask which includes little granules of pumice stone mixed with menthol and camphor. This is to get rid of any dead cells and make the skin more receptive to the next stage of the treatment. The therapist will apply this with her fingertips.

It's very pleasant – your skin will feel tingly and it'll clear your nose! It's also very cooling and refreshing.

The mask would not be used on an acne skin, or on broken capillaries.

4. The mask will be removed with damp sponges, and your skin should feel nice and clean. Then the therapist will apply the collagen mask, which looks like a sheet of blotting paper, or finely rolled-out dough, the size of a face and with holes for your eyes, nose and mouth.

She will apply the mask and add something called marine serum to fix it to the face (it actually becomes almost transparent). The marine serum converts the mask into pure, soluble, 100 per cent collagen, which is said to penetrate into the skin by osmosis.

5. The mask will be left on for 20 to 30 minutes. The therapist will cover your eyes with eye pads soaked in witch hazel, and you'll be left to relax for the first half of the time; for the last fifteen minutes the therapist will give you a relaxing shoulder massage (always the most pleasant part of a treatment). During this time, the skin draws in as much collagen as it possibly can.

Incidentally, the mask won't dry out – it will stay moist. And it won't come off if you sneeze! It's very cooling and not at all claustrophobic, feeling rather like a second skin.

6. The collagen mask will then be peeled off in a rolled-up tissue – when it's taken off it feels like chamois leather.

7. You will then be given a massage with 02 night cream if your skin is dry; if your skin is normal to oily the therapist will apply an 02 marine mask. 02 comes from the spleen of cattle, and is very rich in red corpuscles. This is said to increase the skin's capacity to take in oxygen by 475 per cent.

AFTER
- Let the skin relax for five to ten minutes before applying make-up.
- As with all facials, your hair may suffer slightly from being tied back.

RESULTS
Your skin will look smooth and glowing, and the effects will last for days. Incidentally, a collagen facial should not bring out too many impurities as it's not deep-cleansing.

Home Care ✍

The therapist should be able to recommend products to use at home.

Further Information ✍

The following companies offer collagen mask facials and will give details of salons offering them:

Thalgo, Thalgo House, Tranquil Passage, Blackheath Village, London SE3 0BJ. Tel: 01–852 7472/3.

G. M. Collin, Beeston Grange, Sandy, Beds. SG19 1PG. Tel: (0767) 82288.

MAN APPEAL?   **Yes** – especially for the neck and eye area. Men age, too!   PLEASURE RATING   +1

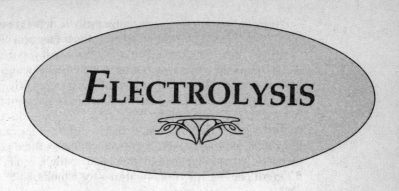

ELECTROLYSIS

The Facts

WHAT IS IT?

Electrolysis (or, more accurately, short-wave diathermy) is described as 'the only permanent method of hair removal'. Electrolysis dates back to 1875, when Charles E. Michel, an American opthalmologist, devised an effective way to remove ingrowing eyelashes from patients about to undergo eye surgery. He discovered that by passing an electrical current down the follicle of the eyelash, the eyelash didn't grow back.

Realising that many women suffer from superfluous hair, he thought it would be a marvellous idea to pass his treatment on to the beauty business. But in those days the treatment was rather crude: it was a galvanic form of electrolysis which chemically decomposed the hair follicle, making regrowth impossible. But because it destroyed part of the tissue around the area, it often left the patient with craters in the skin. Not ideal! The method was also very slow.

In 1916 Professor M. Kree improved the technique by devising a machine which could use ten needles at once and which cut down the treatment time from three minutes per follicle to just one. And eight years later, in 1924, Dr H. Brodier of Paris invented 'thermolysis' – a high frequency method using heat to destroy the papilla (through which the hair receives nourishment) by cauterising and disabling it without damaging the outer layer of skin. The hair is then removed very easily. Thermolysis – or short-wave diathermy – is the most common form of treatment used today.

Electrolysis can be a very lengthy process: whether or not the hairs grow back depends on whether the hair roots are destroyed, and that can depend on what the hair was doing when it was removed – that is, whether it was still growing. Yet, in a recent survey, it was found to be the most frequently requested treatment. One therapist explained: 'It's not a pleasant treatment to have but people subject themselves to some discomfort in order to get rid of unwanted hair. And as they can see the regrowth recessing over a period of time, their confidence increases – they begin to hold their head up high, smile, become a different person. It's very rewarding for a therapist.'

WHERE CAN YOU TRY IT?
● In beauty salons (a few do mainly electrolysis, but most will offer a range of treatments and may simply have some therapists who specialise in electrolysis)
● At health farms
● At special clinics (eg Tao)

HOW MUCH SHOULD IT COST?
Treatment is usually priced according to the length of the treatment. Expect to pay around £8 to £10 for fifteen minutes.

HOW OFTEN SHOULD YOU HAVE IT?
This depends on the sensitivity of your skin and its healing rate. If the skin is very sensitive and not healing very quickly, you'll probably be asked to come back every three weeks. If, however, the skin heals quite quickly and you have a lot of hair to remove, you might be able to have a treatment every fortnight or even every week.

The therapist will also want to give the treated hair a good chance to reappear before you return to the salon: hair must be long enough so that the therapist can tell which way it's growing under the skin – at least ¼ inch (6 mm).

After each treatment any regrown hair will become finer and less noticeable.

HOW LONG SHOULD A TREATMENT TAKE?
The therapist will probably start you off with a ten to fifteen minute treatment. But she'll be watching closely to see how your skin reacts – if it becomes red during treatment, she'll stop so that she won't overdo it.

You'll probably be asked to come back in two weeks' time, and if your skin has healed well the next treatment might take up to half an hour.

HOW LONG SHOULD IT TAKE BEFORE YOU GET RESULTS?

This depends on the amount of hair, the texture, and the cause of the hair growth.

If you've never tampered with the hair, and it's simply excess hair that you feel is socially unacceptable, the therapist should be able to remove it all quite successfully after a few treatments.

If, however, the hairs have been caused by hormonal changes in the body, you may not see a dramatic change at all. Even though removed hairs may not grow back, you may get new hairs growing elsewhere.

If you've previously tweezed out the hair, it will be very strong and will probably need a much stronger current to remove it. It will also be a lot deeper in the skin, and far more persistent, growing back more quickly and more often. Incidentally, never tweeze out a very fair or fine hair, which probably isn't too noticeable: it too will grow a lot thicker and coarser!

DO TRY ELECTROLYSIS:

1. if you have any surplus hair which upsets or embarrasses you – even if it's just one stray hair on the chin. Electrolysis can be used to remove unwanted hair from any part of the body except within the ear and nose. Therapists work most often on the face, arms, legs, bikini line, tummy and breasts.

DON'T TRY ELECTROLYSIS:

1. if you want to remove a hair from a mole (unless your doctor says it's okay).
2. if you are under 16 or over 80.
3. if your legs have varicose veins – although a therapist should be able to work with care on legs if you have just the odd vein.
4. around the nipple if you are pregnant or have just had a baby.
5. *anywhere* just prior to and during your period – you'll be very sensitive. If you must have treatment, then make sure you tell the therapist so she can turn down the current and treat you for less time.

AND YOU **MUST** CHECK WITH YOUR DOCTOR FIRST:

1. if you have a pacemaker – electrolysis could interfere with the frequency.

2. if you are diabetic. If a doctor agrees, remember you'll have a slower healing rate so you should have fewer treatments and lower currents.

3. if you have epilepsy – the therapist would have to be very cautious.

4. if you have any heart problems.

5. if you have any other medical problems, skin disorders or diseases such as eczema.

6. if you are pregnant or have just had a baby. Though electrolysis should be safe up to around seven months (when you'll start becoming more sensitive), the therapist will probably advise you to be patient and see if the hair disappears once you have had your baby. Quite often, superfluous hair will disappear within a couple of months, just like a pregnancy mask (pigmentation in skin), though in some cases it can take up to two years.

HOW CAN YOU TELL IF A THERAPIST IS TRAINED?

1. Because electrolysis can cause scarring if done by an untrained therapist, it's best to ask your doctor or one of the organisations listed on page 61 to recommend a qualified operator.

2. Beauty therapy examiners are very particular about electrolysis, because potentially it's the most dangerous of all treatments. If a student can't probe properly – if she can't put the needle into the follicle correctly – she automatically fails.

3. It's also worth remembering that therapists train by practising treatments on one another. So you can be certain your therapist knows exactly what electrolysis feels like; she will therefore be very careful and sympathetic.

WHAT SHOULD THE THERAPIST ASK YOU?

1. If you have had any previous electrolysis treatment. If so, where, for how long, and the date of your last treatment. She'll want to keep a record of your progress; and from this information she will be able to gauge how successful previous treatments have been, as well as noting any scarring so that she can prove she isn't responsible for it.

If you've been going to a salon for two or three years and you haven't had much success with electrolysis, she will then try to determine why.

2. Where you want treatment. Most people choose electrolysis for the face, but some people opt for it to remove hair from legs, bikini line, underarms, around the nipple (but never on the pigmented areas) and eyebrows.

3. When you first noticed unwanted hair. If you've always had it,

but have only just decided to have it removed, it's probably hereditary, or associated with people of your race. But if superfluous hair has suddenly appeared, it is probably due to hormonal changes in the body – due to puberty, pregnancy, the menopause, or from taking drugs such as birth control pills or cortisone. Hair will never start growing for no apparent reason.

Pregnancy can stimulate hair growth in any area (which should disappear naturally after the pregnancy is over); during puberty girls often develop a permanent hair growth which can be treated once puberty is over, or they can develop a temporary hair growth which will disappear once the hormone balance is restored. After the menopause, many women develop some superfluous hair round the chin and upper lip, in a male growth pattern. That is also due to hormone changes in the body.

4. What temporary measures you have used – for example, tweezing, shaving or waxing. How long you've been using these methods, and the date of the last time you used them.

If you've used wax or tweezers for two or three years, the hair will be a great deal stronger than it would be if you had left it alone, since these distort the hair follicle. So effective treatment is going to take a lot longer.

Tweezing and waxing can distort the hair root; cutting or shaving shouldn't, however, make any difference to the coarseness of the hair.

5. The condition and thickness of the hair, and density of hair growth. If the hair is very fine, it's not sitting very deeply in the dermis (the lower part of the skin). As a result, it doesn't have a very good blood supply, it will be very weak, and you won't need as many treatments and as strong a current to destroy it.

An anagen hair, on the other hand, is a growing hair which will normally be deep in the dermis; it will have searched out a very good blood supply for nutrition, and subsequently it will be a lot stronger and more difficult to terminate.

White hair is very much stronger than any other hair, and you'll see a very big bulb at the end when it's removed. Dark-haired people normally have coarser hair than fair-haired people, though hair growing on the chin and upper lip can often be dark in a fair person anyway.

6. The condition of the skin in the area – acne, scars, spots, for example – and whether it's dry or sensitive. If you have acne, the therapist would avoid pustular areas so that she doesn't spread them. If the skin is sensitive, the therapist would probably give slightly less treatment than for someone with normal skin, because the skin would react far more quickly.

7. Whether you are currently having any medical treatment. The therapist will be able to tell whether you should get your doctor's

advice before proceeding with electrolysis. It's imperative that you are totally honest with the therapist otherwise if your hair isn't disappearing as it should, she won't know why.

8. Whether you are on the pill. This could affect hair growth.

9. Whether you have any children, and the date of your last pregnancy.

SO YOU THINK ELECTROLYSIS SOUNDS GHASTLY . . .

The ancient Egyptians were completely hairless – men and women shaved their heads and used razors and depilatories to remove hair from other parts of their body. Pumice has also been found in Egyptian tombs, which suggests they used that to rub away hair too. (The problem with this method – still used today for removing hair from the legs – is that if you rub the skin too much you'll be very sore afterwards and the hair will eventually grow back in different directions!)

The ancient Turks used a mixture of quicklime and arsenic, with a few drops of rose water added – which they called Rusma.

The ancient Greeks and Romans favoured plucking – even men's beards – along with shaving and depilation. For razors they used sharpened glass, stones and sea-shells.

In 17th-century Britain, *The Ladies Dictionary* advised women to get rid of thick or straggly eyebrows with this mixture: 'Take ivy, gum, Emmets eggs or pincent cosphonie, leeches burnt, half an ounce, grind and mingle with the blood of a frog and annoint the superfluous hair and it will come off.'

In the 18th century, *The Queen's Closet Opened* suggested: 'Take the shells of 52 eggs, beat them small and distill them with a good fire, then with water, annoint yourself where you would have the hair off.' Another recipe offered for hair removal was a poultice of powdered cat dung mixed with strong vinegar.

In 1858 an American named Madame Lola Montez published a beauty book in which she advised spreading gum resin and pitch to a strip of leather and applying it to the hair, ripping it off quickly after three minutes.

And in 1912 American dermatologists began using a chemical depilatory called thallium acetate. Many patients developed reactions such as complete hair loss of the scalp, severe pains in the legs, feet and abdomen, temporary blindness, and multiple neuritis!

WHAT SHOULD YOU ASK THE THERAPIST?
Whether she sterilises her needles or uses disposable ones.
Although salons should have good sterilising equipment – and
local councils lay down ground rules for sterilisation in busi-
nesses which carry out electrolysis, ear piercing, acupuncture
and tattooing – it's safest to minimise the risk of infection by
insisting that your therapist uses a disposable needle.

You'll be able to check that she's using disposable needles as
they come individually packed (Sterex and Blair are probably the
most common), and the therapist will have to break the seal to
use one.

A Typical Electrolysis Treatment 🍃

BEFORE
● The hair must be about ⅛–¼ inch (3–6 mm) long so that the
therapist can tell in which direction the hair follicle is growing.
You should let the hair grow for at least 48 hours before visiting
the salon.
● Though the therapist will cleanse the area before she begins
the treatment, it's best to go for your treatment with a clean skin
free of make-up.
● If you are particularly nervous about the treatment, you could
always ask the therapist if she would remove a couple of hairs just
to show you what electrolysis feels like. You shouldn't be
charged for this.

DURING
1. You will be asked to lie on a couch and the therapist will
explain briefly what the treatment involves. She will then examine the area through a magnifying lamp, angled over the bed, to
check that it is all right to give you a treatment, and to examine the
hair.
2. First she will prepare the area by cleaning it with an antiseptic
liquid. She will blot the area, and choose the correct needle for
your hair growth.
3. She will then insert the needle – which is very fine – just under
the hair, in the same direction, into the hair follicle and down to
the base. Once she's satisfied it's in the right position – she will be
able to feel the needle going in very smoothly if the angle is
correct – she will press a button to release a very slight current to

remove the hair and, hopefully, discourage it from regrowing by destroying the root.

The current dries out the hair bulb and cuts off the blood supply, and the hair will detach itself from the bulb. The therapist will withdraw the needle, and with a pair of tweezers glide the hair out of the follicle.

You might feel anything from a slight sensation to sharp injection-like discomfort as the current is released – everyone is different. (Some people apparently fall asleep during a treatment!) But you shouldn't feel the hair being removed as it is 'dead' by this time. If you do feel a tug, it means the therapist is not doing her job correctly!

4. The therapist will work on the area for as long as she decides is appropriate, constantly checking on the condition of the skin and that you are not finding the treatment too uncomfortable.

When she decides you've had sufficient electrolysis for one day, take her word for it – never insist she continue! If you overdo treatment it will prolong the healing rate and could even cause scarring.

5. When she has finished, the therapist will sterilise the area with an antiseptic liquid such as Savlon, blot the area again and apply some antiseptic cream. She'll also advise you on aftercare – see below.

AFTER

• You might get very tiny red pinpricks where the hairs have been removed, or very slight swelling (which is part of the healing process). Both will normally go away within 24 hours.

• If you develop any allergic reaction, spots or a lot of itching or discomfort, you should go back to the salon so the therapist can determine the cause. This is, however, fairly uncommon.

• The area you've had treated may become reddened afterwards – it depends on the amount of current needed to remove your hair. This should disappear within twenty minutes to an hour of the treatment.

If you get any redness or swelling, apply witch hazel to the area for ten minutes every two hours, using cotton wool pads. If your skin is dry, apply rosewater in the same way.

• It's best not to put any water on the area – if water isn't completely clean it could cause an infection.

• Tiny scabs may develop a couple of days later, where some hairs have been treated. They will fall off naturally – never pick them or rub them off.

• Don't touch, scratch or pick the area.

• Don't have a hot bath or wash the area with soap for 24 hours.

If you want to wash, apply cool boiled water to the area with cotton wool pads. The pores will be enlarged where hairs have been removed, and anything applied to the body could find its way into the pores and cause infection.

● Never squeeze any spots which might appear – apply an antiseptic cream such as Savlon or a gel such as Witch Doctor.

● Don't sunbathe for 36 hours after a treatment – the skin's pigmentation will have been altered and you may get light or dark patches, which are permanent! You will also be more likely to burn as the skin will be sensitive after this heat treatment.

● If you must use make-up after a treatment, use calamine lotion as a base for the first 24 hours.

● If you get any bruising after a treatment, complain to the therapist.

RESULTS

One treatment will not be sufficient, but you'll find that after each treatment the hair will become progressively finer and less noticeable. You may see new hairs sprouting at any time up from two to six weeks after treatment. Any that appear earlier are more likely to be hairs that weren't treated.

You can stop having treatment and resume from where you left off at any time provided you don't remove hairs yourself in the meantime – you can, of course, cut them.

Eventually, provided there is no medical reason for the hair growth, the area should be free of hair.

Home Care ✍

In between treatments, don't shave, wax or tweeze any new hairs – cut them with nail scissors. You may bleach them, but you should allow them to grow darker before your next electrolysis treatment.

Further Information ✍

Different methods of electrolysis are practised at different salons, including 'the blend' – a combination of galvanic electrolysis and short-wave diathermy, which is used extensively in some parts of

HAIR TODAY . . .

There are three different stages of hair growth, and whether or not a hair will grow back depends at which stage it is removed. Once she has removed a hair, the therapist will be able to tell, from its appearance, at which stage it was.

- **Anagen** is the growing stage. If the therapist removes a hair at anagen – when it is still connected to the blood supply – she's most likely to destroy part of it or permanently remove it. The majority of hairs are at anagen, because it takes about four to six weeks for the hair to grow on the body (on the head, though, it takes two to five years).
  A hair removed at anagen has a bulb at the end.

- **Catagen** is the transitional phase, when the hair detaches itself from the blood supply and starts to break down. It takes about fourteen days for the hair to move up the hair follicle, so you get very few hairs at this stage.
  A hair removed at catagen has a little tail at the end.

- **Telogen** is the resting stage. Hair stays in the follicle for three to five months, waiting to be shed. It will then either be shed normally or will be pushed out by a new anagen hair coming up. If a therapist removes a hair at telogen she's far less likely to remove the hair for good because the hair has stopped growing.
  A hair removed at telogen has a blunt end.

the US, Holland and New Zealand – and the Sylvia Lewis Method (available in twenty countries including Australia) which uses a more moderated current and a specially designed rigid L-shaped needle (with this method a therapist may be able to treat you for longer periods and almost daily).

But whatever method of electrolysis is used, it's the skill of the operator which is most important. A good operator will choose the machine that's right for her, and she should never burn the skin.

If you develop any scars after a treatment – *sue*! It means the therapist has been negligent: she has applied too much current, or too high a current, or has kept her finger on the current button when probing the follicle (she should only release current when the needle is in position), or she has probed at the wrong angle.

For details of qualified therapists you can contact BABTAC (see page 11) or one of the following:

The British Association of Electrolysists, 28 Quakers Mede, Haddenham, Bucks. HP17 8EB. Tel: 0844 290721

Institute of Electrolysis, 251 Seymour Grove, Manchester M16 0DS.

Your doctor should also be able to recommend a therapist.
Electrolysis can also be used to treat thread veins (see page 154).

MAN APPEAL?   **Yes!**
● for removing hairs resulting from nicks from misdirected razor blades and sensitive skin.
● for thinning or removing beards to make light work of shaving – though this treatment may take quite a while as hair shaved regularly will be very coarse.
● for removing hair from backs (especially actors and athletes).
● for removing eyebrows which grow over the bridge of the nose, or are too thick and bushy.
● for, in older men, removing hairs from the outside of the ears and the top of the nose.

PLEASURE RATING   −5

EYEBROW SHAPING

The Facts

WHAT IS IT?
It might be argued that everyone's natural eyebrow shape should suit them, but unfortunately this isn't always the case. Sometimes the natural fall of the eyebrows isn't at all complementary to the face – the brows may be too thick, for example, or completely the wrong shape.

Fashion, of course, plays a large part too. In the sixties it was considered fashionable to have a thin eyebrow line, and women often shaved or waxed the whole lot off and drew in a line with eyebrow pencil. Today, on the other hand, thick brows are very fashionable – unfortunate for those sixties trendies, who are finding it difficult to grow their eyebrows back after years of plucking! But even if your brows are luxuriant, you may still benefit from having them shaped expertly.

These days therapists pluck or use wax or electrolysis to shape brows. You can have a shaping alone, or you can see if it is – or can be – incorporated into a facial.

WHERE CAN YOU TRY IT?
- At beauty salons
- At health farms and clubs
- At some hairdressers
- On board ships, etc

HOW MUCH SHOULD IT COST?
Around £5.

HOW OFTEN SHOULD YOU HAVE IT?

Eyebrow shaping is something you may need just once – then you can regularly trim stray hairs yourself, or have them removed for you the next time you visit the salon.

HOW LONG SHOULD IT TAKE?

Up to fifteen minutes, depending on the method used. If you have electrolysis, you might have only five minutes on each eyebrow at first (see Electrolysis, page 51).

DO TRY EYEBROW SHAPING:

1. if you've always been unhappy about the shape of your brows – if, for instance, they meet across the bridge of the nose. If you undertake a major reshape yourself, you run the risk of making a mess of it, so it's a good idea to have a therapist start you off.
2. if you want to remove straggly hairs permanently – in which case you'd have to consider a course of electrolysis.

HOW CAN YOU TELL IF A THERAPIST IS GOOD?

She will pay attention to the shape of your face and eyes before she starts work on your brows. She will also work out how to give you the best possible shape using the eyebrows you've got.

WHAT SHOULD YOU ASK THE THERAPIST?

Which method would be most suitable. Plucking and waxing are temporary, whereas electrolysis can be a permanent hair removal (as long as you don't tamper between sessions). Bear in mind that plucking and waxing will shape the eyebrows in just one session, but electrolysis will take several as only a few hairs can be removed at a time.

A Typical Eyebrow Shaping Using Tweezers ✍

BEFORE

● Remove contact lenses – your eyes may water.

DURING

1. After you've discussed your requirements with the therapist, you will lie down or sit comfortably, with a gown and towel covering your clothes.

2. The therapist will remove all make-up from the brows, and will apply a menthol cream around the area. This will soothe the skin and make plucking easier and less uncomfortable for you.

3. If the brows are very thick and coarse, it's less painful if hot pads of damp cotton wool are placed over the brows beforehand. This allows the pores to relax and the hairs to come out of the follicle easier.

4. The therapist will brush the eyebrows to see the direction of the hair growth and exact shape of brows. She will then pull taut the skin in the area she's going to pluck, and will remove the hair in quick, light strokes, in the direction of the hair growth.

This shouldn't be too uncomfortable, though your eyes might smart!

5. Once the eyebrows have been shaped, she may place cotton pads soaked in mild astringent on them to soothe the area.

6. She should then show you in the mirror to make sure you're satisfied with the shape.

AFTER
- You might be a little bit red, but this will soon fade.

RESULTS
The right shape of eyebrows will give the eyes more definition and will enhance the application of make-up to show off the face.

Further Information ✒

Many make-up books deal with eyebrow shaping – they may help you decide on the shape you would like.

MAN APPEAL? **Yes** – for eyebrows that meet over the bridge of the nose.

PLEASURE RATING −2

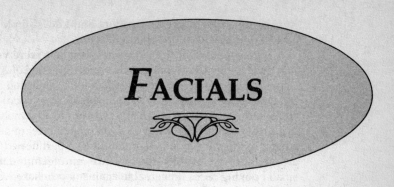

FACIALS

The Facts ✍

WHAT IS A FACIAL?
Facials vary considerably, from a soothing 'mini-facial' which may combine cleansing, toning and moisturising with plenty of relaxing massage (around the hairline, temples, under the chin, neck and shoulders), to a deep-cleansing facial which can involve everything from exfoliation (removing the top, dead, layer of skin) to the removal of blackheads.

Facials also depend, to some extent, on the products the therapist uses in her salon. Each cosmetic company has its own range of products, which are applied in a certain way: facials you might be offered include Clarins, DeCleor, René Guinot, Thalgo, and G. M. Collin. Some facials are purely manual, others involve the use of, for example, a high-frequency machine to 'spark' spots and dry them out.

When choosing a facial, you should bear in mind the reason you want one (as a relaxing treat, or because your skin is in poor condition, for example), and the kind of skin you have (whether it's dry, sensitive, young, ageing, etc). Your therapist should examine your skin and advise you on the facial that would be most beneficial.

WHERE CAN YOU HAVE ONE?
- At beauty salons
- At health farms and clubs
- On board ships, etc
- At a Clarins Skincare Centre in a large department store – at time of writing Selfridges, Oxford Street, and House of Fraser,

Kensington High Street, in London, and Lewis's in Manchester and Glasgow, with more planned.

A representative of the company says: 'We were very aware that there were many women who were frightened of going into a salon, frightened about a very professional, polished approach, but who were keen to improve their skin. So they would go into a store and speak to a therapist about home treatments. . . We came up with the idea of having a circular counter in department stores, in the middle of which would be a partitioned treatment area, where we would give twenty-minute mini-facials. The small booking fee is redeemable against a purchase.

'We are providing a service between the shop and the salon, introducing women who are keen to introduce a comprehensive skincare routine to a mini version of a salon treatment. It's a very good stepping stone to salons.'

HOW MUCH SHOULD IT COST?
This varies considerably – expect to pay anything from £8 upwards.

HOW OFTEN SHOULD YOU HAVE ONE?
This depends on the kind of facial and the condition of the skin – your therapist should advise you. As a treat, try a facial once a month – especially if you are over 30 – or even a mini-facial every two weeks.

HOW LONG SHOULD IT TAKE?
This depends on the facial – from half an hour for a mini-facial to an hour for a full facial.

DO HAVE A FACIAL:
1. if your skin needs a tonic.
2. if you need to relax. All facials include a degree of massage, while the way products are applied is also very soothing.
3. if you want your skin in good condition for a special event – though remember that facials are stimulating and could bring out impurities (ie pimples and blackheads). It's best to have your facial a day before the event.
4. if you want to keep your skin in good condition – though you'll need to take your therapist's advice on home care, too.
5. if you live or work in a centrally heated or air-conditioned atmosphere, which can play havoc with your skin.

6. whatever your skin type. There are so many different types of facial that you should find one suitable for your skin, even if it's highly sensitive (the therapist would take care not to use any harsh or perfumed products).

DON'T HAVE A FACIAL:
1. if it includes the use of electrical equipment and you have a pacemaker etc. (For a full list of what therapists call 'contra-indications' – ie people who shouldn't have certain treatments – see Cathiodermie, page 34.)

A Typical Clarins Double Serum Facial ✍

SUITABLE FOR:
● skins which are sometimes under stress and subjected to pollution – ideal for city-dwellers.
● most skin types – though not skins with severe congestion, such as acne sufferers.
● anyone aged 25 plus.

YOU'D NEED TO HAVE IT:
● once a week at first, if you've neglected your skin, for four weeks, followed by treatments once a month and eventually every six weeks.

IT TAKES:
● about an hour.

IT COSTS:
● from £15 to £20.

BEFORE
● *Don't* arrive wearing make-up, if possible.

DURING
1. First of all you'll be asked to undress and lie on a couch. Take off your shirt and anything that might get creased. If you keep

your bra on, the therapist will simply pull down your straps during the treatment. Your hair will be pulled back and covered with a towel or headband and scarf.

2. The therapist will remove any make-up you are wearing, then cleanse your face twice. Your skin can get quite grubby, and pick up a lot of dust and pollution, simply travelling to the salon!

3. She'll now tone the skin, using two pads of cotton wool – one in each hand – to remove all trace of cleanser, then blot your face with a tissue. Your skin should now feel clean.

It's essential the therapist uses both hands evenly on the face – if she treats one side and then the other, it feels uneven, but if she treats both sides at the same time the effect is much more pleasant and balanced. It's also important that she keeps her hands moving in a soothing rhythm.

4. The next stage in many facial and body treatments is exfoliation – peeling the skin – which involves the use of different types of product, applied to the skin and gently rubbed off. This takes with it a lot of debris which still remains on the surface of the skin even after thorough cleansing and toning. Don't worry though – it won't remove a tan!

If you have very sensitive skin, the therapist would peel it off very gently, using a gentle product which isn't 'gritty' and doesn't contain anything that might dry out the skin.

She will place a tissue underneath your neck to catch the debris, and apply an exfoliating cream not only over the face but also over the lips, neck and cleavage – areas which show a woman's age, but which we tend to neglect!

She will leave the cream for a minute, then roll it off gently with her fingertips.

5. She will now apply an essential oil (see page 21) mixed with a base oil (invariably Vitamin E), and give you a massage. Every therapist has her own massage technique – the one described below is simply an example.

There are hundreds of essential oils to choose from and it depends what the therapist is trying to achieve. For the face, particularly for oily skins, she might use geranium, sage or rosemary. All of these are natural antiseptics and help to calm down the production of sebum (the greasy substance which lubricates the skin, and overproduction of which leads to blackheads).

She will massage the front neck area then round the back of the neck, which is a stress area. She'll also work around the eyes – another area of stress – and gently up into the pressure point on the bridge of the nose, where tension can settle, then across the brow and on to the temple itself. Pressure on the temple should be very gentle; if it's too heavy, it may give you a headache.

6. The therapist will tone your skin, removing some of the oil, then apply double serum, described as a 'total vitamin for the skin'. It is said to balance the moisture level, help the oxygen level and regenerate the skin. The therapist will press and roll the product into your skin, even around the eyes. (Incidentally, oil should never be applied around the eyes unless the area is protected first: the oil can be drawn into the mucus membrane which can cause swelling and puffiness.)

7. She will now cover your eyes with pads and apply a moisturising face mask to the face, neck and shoulders. Unlike some masks which 'set', this mask will stay moist.

8. After removing the mask, she will then apply a 'tightening' ampoule (a condensed mixture of different oils and vitamins which will penetrate the skin) to firm and tighten the face. It should keep the skin strengthened and in good condition for four to twelve months.

9. She will finish by applying a little tinted moisturiser, and some Beauty Flash – an instant pick-me-up which smoothes the skin as well as acting as a protection.

FACIAL EXPRESSIONS

DO:
- try a facial in a salon. A therapist can apply products in a way you can't yourself.
- ask questions. There's nothing worse than lying on a couch, having products applied to your face, and not knowing what's going on and what those products are doing for you.
- ask the therapist to write down the products she's used, and the ones you should be using at home. The price of your treatment includes as much advice as you need – so make the most of it.
- ask the therapist simply to let you relax if that's what you prefer.

DON'T:
- go back to using products that aren't good for your skin – such as harsh soap (use a water-soluble cleanser instead), or drying, alcohol-based products (you can smell these when you open the bottle; toning lotions with a high alcohol content also feel very cold when applied to the skin). You'll undo all the good work the therapist has carried out in the salon, and waste money!
- neglect your skin because you know someone of 80 who has never used skin products yet has beautiful skin. Her generation wasn't under as much stress in terms of pollution, air-conditioning, central heating etc.

SPOT REDUCTION

If you have very bad acne, it's best to start by going to your doctor. You might need a course of antibiotics, or he or she may refer you to a skin specialist. Your doctor is unlikely, though, to suggest you try a beauty treatment – which is a pity since a good facial, which includes deep-cleansing the skin, steaming it open, pressing out blackheads and finishing with a face mask, can by very beneficial.

A beauty therapist can also do a number of things a skin specialist simply doesn't have the time to do. As well as removing blackheads (which therapists refer to as commedones), she can also teach you how to clean and make-up your skin correctly, advise you on the kind of products you should use at home (such as medicated cover-up creams), and tell you which foods to eat and avoid.

AFTER
- Any impurities lying beneath the surface of the skin may come out – and better out than in!
- It's a pity to have your skin cleaned and then apply heavy make-up. If you can, leave skin alone for the rest of the day, or at least three to four hours.
- Your hair may look a mess if it's been covered up tightly for an hour.

RESULTS
Once you've had a good facial, you'll be hooked!

Home Care ✍

You should always thoroughly cleanse and tone your skin, and moisturise well every morning. A moisturiser will act as protection against pollution, wind and extreme weather conditions; it also allows make-up to sit on the skin without causing any damage – blocking the pores, for example.

The therapist should also advise you on other products you should be using.

MAN APPEAL? Yes	PLEASURE RATING +4

A Typical Cleorderm Facial ✒

SUITABLE FOR:
- all kinds of skins, including acne skins.

YOU'D NEED TO HAVE IT:
- three times over a period of ten days to see results, followed by a treatment every four to six weeks, depending on your skin.

IT TAKES:
- about one to one and a half hours.

IT COSTS:
- £15 to £25 a treatment.

BEFORE
- *Don't* arrive wearing heavy make-up.

DURING
1. You will be asked to undress (as before) and lie on your back on a couch. The therapist will start by cleansing and removing any make-up, then she'll tone the face and upper chest.
2. Before continuing with the facial, she will now carry out 'back diagnostics'. These are based on acupuncture points and lymphatic drainage. You will be asked to turn on to your front, and she will massage the nerve endings found in spaces between your vertebrae on each side of the spine, which should help rid the body of toxins and tone up your internal organs. It will have a pleasantly relaxing effect on you, and give her a chance to examine your skin.
3. You'll now be asked to turn on to your back again, and the therapist will 'peel' your skin, to prepare it for the treatment. If necessary, she may also steam the skin (three to five minutes should be sufficient to open pores sufficiently to remove blackheads).
4. The therapist will use lymphatic drainage to help get rid of toxins and waste from the face and neck, massaging a small amount of an appropriate oil (which will penetrate the skin) into pressure points around the face, neck and shoulders for five minutes.

5. She will now cover the whole neck and face area with a delicate 'patchwork' of creams, which she will massage in lightly for ten minutes. Then she will cover your eyes with gel, followed by eyepads.

6. The therapist will then make up an aromaplasm mask – a kind of warm brown poultice, wrapped in gauze – which she will place over the creams to help them penetrate. One mask will be placed across the forehead, eyes and nose; a second over the neck and chin (only your nostrils will be exposed).

She will leave this mask on your skin for ten minutes, staying with you throughout.

7. After lifting off the mask and wiping the skin lightly with damp cotton wool, she will then apply a clay mask for a further ten minutes, which she will wipe off with a damp sponge.

8. Finally, she will apply a small amount of moisturiser to the face, neck and shoulders.

AFTER
- Your skin should feel clean and fresh.
- Your hair may look a mess.
- Leave the skin free of make-up for at least three hours.

RESULTS
Your whole system should be rebalanced, making you feel relaxed. Regular treatments may also ensure your skin ages as slowly as possible.

MAN APPEAL?   **Yes** – especially if you have acne.

PLEASURE RATING   **+2**

G5

The Facts

WHAT IS IT?

G5 is a mechanical kind of massage, using gyratory vibrators, which you'd choose if you wanted to get rid of areas of solid fat, on the thighs for example. Unlike a hand massage (see Massage, page 106), G5 is usually only applied to specific problem areas. It has the advantage, though, of producing far quicker, deeper results than a hand massage could.

The machine has a variety of different 'heads', which are all used on different areas – from hard, knobbly ones to break up large areas of fat, to foam ones to gently massage the stomach. Massage with these heads stimulates the flow of blood and lymph; this increases the circulation within the muscles and encourages fresh blood to flow into the area and toxins (waste products) to be eliminated easily.

Some salons prefer to use only manual massage, so it's best to enquire first.

WHERE CAN YOU TRY IT?

- At most beauty salons
- At health farms and health clubs
- On board ships, etc

HOW MUCH SHOULD IT COST?
From around £8 per treatment.

HOW OFTEN SHOULD YOU HAVE IT?
Once a week for a few weeks until the condition improves, then once a month. Or try one a day for three days to get the treatment off the ground.

HOW LONG SHOULD A TREATMENT TAKE?
Anything from ten to thirty minutes.

DO TRY G5:
1. if you have fatty areas, say on the thighs and hips, that need to be softened and broken up.
2. if you have a lot of tension – on the neck and shoulders, for example. It will relax muscles, release tension and help to restore muscles to their normal condition.
3. if you have dry, scaly skin. There are certain kinds of G5 that can be used for speeding up blood circulation, and this will, in turn, speed up the production of new-skin cells on the area. You could, for instance, use G5 lightly on your scalp or elbows.
4. in conjunction with slimming treatments or exercise. It can be used to heat up local areas prior to certain treatments, like Slendertone (see page 138) or wax treatments (see page 164), for example. It will also help the breakdown of fat cells and increase elimination of waste products.
   Some people have a few sessions of G5 followed by a few sessions of Slendertone – the G5 breaks up the fat and the Slendertone tones up the muscles.
5. if you're an athlete and want to relax tension in the muscles after exercise.
6. if you've overdone the exercise and have cramps. G5 will release the tension in between the muscles.

DON'T TRY G5:
1. if you have varicose veins or broken capillaries on your skin.
2. if you have any kind of inflammation or irritation.
3. if you have any recent wounds or scars.
4. if you have broken any bones recently.
5. if you have had any recent operations.
6. if you have any heart problems.
7. if you are of a nervous disposition – though the therapist could proceed with caution.
8. on bony areas, where there is no fat to cover the area.

HOW CAN YOU TELL IF A THERAPIST IS GOOD?

She will make sure that you are not uncomfortable, and that the pressure of the G5 is not too hard. The pressure should be firm and the head of the vibrator should be kept flat. It's best to use on specific muscles for only four to eight minutes – the strokes may be directed along the length of the muscles or sometimes can remain still.

A Typical G5 Treatment &

BEFORE
- *Don't* have a big meal.
- *Don't* have a leg wax if having G5 on legs.
- *Do* have a sauna or steam bath to soften the skin tissues.

DURING
1. You'll be asked to undress. If, for example, you are having G5 on the thighs and buttocks, you'll have to take off your tights. You can keep your knickers on – the therapist will simply pull them down when treating the buttock area.
2. You will then lie on a couch on your back, and the therapist will apply a thin layer of talcum powder to the area to be treated. This makes the vibrator heads move more smoothly over the area.
3. The therapist will then assess the muscle tone and choose the right head to treat the area. Different heads do different things: foam applicators are used for the abdomen or muscles not surrounded by fat; hard rubber applicators are used on areas liberally covered with fat or areas covered with muscle (for athletes or muscular men). Other heads include one shaped like a football which is used only for very solid fat; a lightweight football-shaped disc that can be used for a colon massage on the abdomen; and a multi-spiked applicator that is used for the scalp.
4. The therapist can either use straight, stroking movements or circular kneading movements. But no movement should hurt – if it's uncomfortable, tell the therapist. If you get any redness it means the treatment is beneficial, but you shouldn't get any bruising.

AFTER
- If you are bruised after a treatment, tell the therapist – it means she's given too hard a treatment.

RESULTS
G5 massage will create a feeling of warmth, which will give rise to a feeling of relaxation – just like hand massage. In time, solid areas of fat should become softer until they disperse, but G5 must be used in conjunction with diet and possibly electric treatment (ie Slendertone, see page 138).

MAN APPEAL?   **Yes** – ideal after exercise.

PLEASURE RATING   **0**

HEALTH FARMS

The Facts ✎

WHAT ARE THEY?

Health farms these days concentrate more on relieving stress than on strict dieting. The days of nasty enemas, fasting, and the resultant sneaking out to the local shops for sustenance are now, happily, a thing of the past.

So it's not surprising that more and more people are choosing to spend their annual holiday being pampered at a health farm, away from pressures of work or family, rather than fight with holiday crowds on Continental beaches. Many, in fact, return year after year.

You'll find all kinds of people at a health farm, from housewives who need a break from the kids, to businessmen and women who need to get away from the pressures of work. You'll even – if you're lucky, rub dressing-gowned shoulders with a celebrity or two!

Most health farms are in beautiful country-house settings, with a wide range of beauty treatments, exercise classes and sports available throughout the day. The rooms are comfortable and, unlike many holiday hotels, you won't have any difficulty booking single rooms. The atmosphere is usually very relaxed, with most people lounging around in tracksuits or dressing gowns.

You'll find the main topic of conversation tends to be the next meal, but the food – much of which is crunchy and filling – shouldn't leave you thinking of ways to slip out to the nearest chippy!

Every day, as well as standard treatments, you can make your own choice from a selection of other treatments and activities: discos in the evening, art classes, interesting lectures on all sorts of topics are just some of the things you may find.

HOW WILL YOU FIND THE RIGHT HEALTH FARM FOR YOU?
Health farms have different philosophies: some are beauty-treatment orientated; some concentrate on alternative health cures; while others have a medical bias and are most suitable for people convalescing from illness. Some have resident physicians, others don't. So send off for a selection of brochures and compare what's on offer.

You'll need to remember to consider exactly what is included in the price of your stay, too. Some, for instance, offer a selection of free treatments (say, a sauna, steam bath or a facial plus a body massage for every day of your stay). Others charge for all treatments. Equally, treatment prices vary considerably.

As in most things, it's often a case of 'you get what you pay for'. A smaller, lower-priced health farm, for instance, may not have separate treatment rooms; if you like your privacy, make sure to check.

Of course, you'll also have to consider the location. If you live in London and fancy visiting a health farm in the north of Scotland, for example, remember that the train fare will add a hefty amount to the price of your holiday. On the other hand, if you are choosing a health farm stay as your main holiday, you may want to consider visiting one in another country.

You may be able to save money by sharing a room, or by taking advantage of an introductory offer (but remember to check whether all the treatments you want to try will be available to you).

If you're unfamiliar with beauty treatments, it might be a good idea to try out a top-to-toe treatment (see page 159) at your local beauty salon first. This will give you a taste of the kind of treatments you'll be able to sample at a health farm. The joy of a health farm, though, is that people are only too happy to tell you about treatments they have enjoyed, and you will no doubt be more adventurous than you might otherwise be.

WILL YOU STARVE?
Despite horror stories you're bound to have heard, you won't starve at a health farm. The food these days is terrific – fresh, appetising, and attractively presented – and in many cases you can choose how little or how much you eat. Dishes are often

calorie counted for your convenience, but it's up to you whether you want to lose weight.

It's certainly a sign of the times that few health farms these days believe in fasting – and many even feature a picture of their dinner-time spread in their brochure!

And if you don't need to lose weight, you may even be allowed wine with your dinner. If that's important to you, be sure to check in advance!

A TYPICAL DAY'S LOW-CALORIE MENU AT A HEALTH FARM

Breakfast: bowl of cereal with skimmed milk, half an apple, and a cup of decaffeinated coffee

Lunch: clear soup, small dish of cheese and tomato-topped vegetables and a plate of interesting and crunchy (but dressing-free) salads, followed by fresh fruit or jelly

Supper: soup, fish or poultry with two vegetables, low-calorie sweet

Drinks: mineral water and limited amounts of decaffeinated coffee allowed during the day

---

HOW MUCH WILL IT COST?
About the same as a good holiday. Price depends on the amount of luxury you want, the type of room you choose – whether you are prepared to share, for example – the length of your stay, the number of treatments you sample etc. At some health farms some treatments will be included in the price of your room.

HOW LONG SHOULD YOU GO FOR?
If it's your first time, anything from a few days to a week. A few days is generally long enough to unwind and enjoy being pampered; over a week and you could start getting bored – and that could prove an expensive mistake.

If the health farm is easily accessible, see if it does one-day, weekend or short breaks which will give you some idea of whether you would enjoy a longer stay.

WHAT DO YOU NEED TO TAKE?

When you book, you will be sent a list of things you will need to take with you. These are the ones I'd recommend:

• A dressing gown (ideally with large pockets in which you can put your room key and daily schedule). You'll need it to wear over your bra and pants when you go for treatments (it's easier to slip off than a tracksuit), and over your swimsuit if there are no changing facilities by the pool. There's no need to go out and buy a glamorous new one specially. In health farms, anything goes!

• A tracksuit for lounging around between treatments and classes. You might also want to wear your tracksuit bottoms for exercise classes.

• A hairdryer. If you have treatments, your hair may get oily around the hairline; if you go swimming you'll want to wash your hair afterwards; and you may get a bit sticky after an exercise class.

• Aspirins or other medication. Health farm rooms and corridors are usually kept at a very high temperature since people are undressed most of the day, so you may get headaches. The same could apply if you are not used to dieting. Though most establishments have a shop within the grounds, you might find it shut when you need a headache pill, so it's best to come prepared.

• A large towel. You will usually be provided with sufficient towels, but it's a good idea to take along an extra one – you might want to go swimming twice in one morning for example.

• Exercise gear. A leotard (or two) or t-shirts and tracksuit bottoms are sufficient.

• Slippers or casual shoes. Again, there's no need to buy a new pair of slippers unless you really want to. No-one pays much attention to your appearance during the day.

• A watch or clock. You will be expected to have treatments at particular times of the day, so if you think you may want to spend time reading in your room, or walking in the grounds, you will need to have a watch.

• Swimwear.

• Plenty of underwear. You might get hot and sticky after exercising and you may find that oils used in treatments make your underwear sticky. You may also want to keep on your pants for comfort, say, in a steam cabinet or during a Cleortherm treatment (see page 41), so you'll want to change immediately afterwards.

• Reading material, preferably the kind you can pick up and drop whenever you get a chance. You will often find you have the odd half-hour to kill, and it will take your mind off food!

• Appropriate sportswear and equipment.

• Suitable shoes – sturdy ones for walking in the grounds, and trainers if you think you may be tempted to go jogging.

BUT **DON'T** TAKE:
- too much jewellery. You'll have to remove it for treatments anyway.
- too much cash. You will have to leave your room unattended for great chunks of the day, and you don't want to have to carry your handbag around with you everywhere. Most guests just carry around their room key and daily schedule sheet.

WHAT WILL HAPPEN WHEN YOU ARRIVE?

Once you've booked in, you'll be given an appointment for a consultation, at which you'll be asked a comprehensive range of questions about your health: whether you're on any medication, whether you suffer from migraines, whether you have heart or respiratory problems etc. From this, the consultant will be able to advise you on treatments you should avoid or might like to try.

If you say you suffer from headaches, for example, you'd be advised to avoid saunas; if you have a pacemaker or any metal pins you wouldn't be allowed to have any treatments that use electrical currents; if you are on medication you would be advised not to use a sunbed etc.

You'll then be weighed and measured – this is probably the only part of your stay you'll hate! – and your diet discussed: how many calories you will need to stick to if you want to lose weight, for example (though many people these days think of weight loss simply as a bonus).

The consultant will go through all the activities and treatments on offer, explaining what they involve. He or she will then help you plan your itinerary, booking you in for any treatments that are included in the price of your stay, and suggesting others that you might try in between.

If you're not used to exercise, he or she will probably suggest that you start slowly – perhaps just taking a yoga class on your first day. Remember, if you go mad on your first day, you won't be able to move on the second!

THEN WHAT?

You will go away with a daily schedule in your hand and it will be up to you how you fill the hours between your treatments.

Every day you will be able to take part in a selection of exercise classes, lectures etc, often displayed on a blackboard or notice board. The best thing is to look at the options available, pencil in those you really don't want to miss, and plan your days around these and your treatments.

But you'll need to be sensible – don't do two exercise classes one after the other (you want to enjoy your stay, not kill yourself!); and check which activities and treatments *don't* go together (this book should help!).

Remember, too, that you'll benefit more from a *relaxing* stay, so where possible take time to rest in your room, or take a gentle stroll around the building, or maybe sit in the lounge and chat to other residents. You'll generally find people very happy to talk to you, especially about food!

RESULTS
If you make the most of your stay at a health farm, you'll come away relaxed, fit and raring to go. The chances are your eating habits will be much improved, too; after a week of nutritious wholefood you won't fancy tucking into stodge and undoing all the good work.

Many health farms see re-education of your lifestyle as part of their function, and hopefully you'll learn enough about minimising stress to make the effects of your stay long-lasting.

Some of the Major British Health Farms and Clinics and What They Offer ✑

Brooklands Health Farm
Calder House, Garstang, Preston, Lancs. PR3 1QB. Tel: Garstang (09952) 5162.

A small health farm set in five acres of land in Lancashire.

Treatments and activities on offer include aromatherapy, body massage, Cathiodermie, electrolysis, exercise classes, eyelash and brow dye, facials (Clarins), G5, hairdressing, hydrotherapy, infra-red, make-up, manicures, paraffin wax, pedicures, reflexology, sauna, scalp treatments, Slendertone, solarium, spa bath, swimming pool, tennis, Turkish room and waxing.

Prices include all meals and a selection of treatments.

Cedar Falls Health Farm
Bishops Lydeard, Taunton, Somerset TA4 3HR.
Tel: 0823 433233.

A mansion house, dating from 1740, situated in the foothills of the Quantocks and close to Exmoor National Park. It's a two and a half hour journey by car from London.

Treatments and activities on offer include acupuncture, aromatherapy, aromatherapy bath, chiropody, dry ski slope, electrolysis, eyebrow shaping, eyelash and brow tints, exercise classes, facials (Clarins), G5, gymnasium, hairdressing, horse riding, Jacuzzi, manicures, massage, mud packs, osteopathy, paraffin wax baths, pedicures, reflexology, relaxation classes, sauna, Slendertone, steam cabinets, solarium, swimming pool, waxing and yoga.

Prices include meals and a selection of treatments.

Champneys
Tring, Herts. HP23 6HY. Tel: Berkhamsted (04427) 3351

A beautiful mansion, 33 miles from London, established as a health resort in 1925 and set in a 170-acre parkland estate, surrounded by shady beechwood forests, open parkland and traditional English villages.

Enton Hall Clinic
Enton, Near Godalming, Surrey, GU8 5AL. Tel: Wormley (042879) 2233.

A 50-acre property in the depths of the Surrey countryside, Enton Hall is under full-time medical supervision and 'combines medical expertise with healthy alternatives'. It is 38 miles south of London, 4 miles south of Godalming.

Treatments and activities on offer include dietary advice, exercise classes, health evaluation and testing, health lectures, hydrotherapy, Jacuzzi, laboratory tests, massage, physiotherapy, sauna, solarium, steam cabinets, swimming pool.

Prices for a basic health programme depend on the season, from £322–£480 a week.

Grayshott Hall
Grayshott, Near Hindhead, Surrey GU26 6JJ.
Tel: Hindhead (042873) 4331.

A Victorian mansion set in 47 acres of landscaped grounds, about 50 miles south-west of London.

Treatments and activities on offer include aerobics, aromatherapy, blanket wrap, bust treatments, Cathiodermie, chiropody, eyebrow reshape, eyebrow and eyelash tint, facials, faradism, G5, hairdressing, Jacuzzi, jogging, lectures on nutrition and diet, manicure, osteopathy, panthermal, pedicure, physiotherapy, reflexology, relaxation, sauna, Slendertone, solarium, steam cabinet, swimming pool, Swedish hand massage, underwater massage, water exercises, waxing, weight training and yoga.

Prices include a daily massage and one of a selection of heat treatments.

Henlow Grange Health Farm
Henlow, Beds. SG16 6DD. Tel: 0462 811111.

A Georgian manor house which was converted into a health farm in 1961. It is 46 miles north of London, 10 miles north of Luton, and can be reached via the A1.

Treatments and activities on offer include aerobics, aromatherapy, aromatic spa baths, bust treatments, Cathiodermie, Cleortherm, collagen treatments, cycling, diet consultations, electrolysis, eyelash and brow tints, facials (René Guinot, DeCleor, Clarins), faradism, G5, gym instruction, hairdressing, infra-red, make-up and make-up lessons, manicures and nail treatments, men's workout classes, Parafango mud treatment, pedicures, reflexology, relaxation classes, saunas, seaweed baths, steam cabinets, swimming pool, vacuum suction, wax baths, waxing and yoga.

Prices include all meals and a selection of treatments.

Inglewood Health Hydro
Kintbury, Berks. RG12 0SL. Tel: Hungerford (0488) 82022.

Mentioned in the Domesday Book, Inglewood was one of the great houses of the Knights Templar during the crusade of 1108. It was converted to a health hydro in 1975, and is set in 50 acres of Berkshire Downs.

Treatments and activities on offer include aerobics, aromatherapy, ear piercing, electrolysis, eyebrow and eyelash tinting, facials, G5, gymnasium, hairdressing, Jacuzzi, jogging, keep fit, lectures on nutrition and stress control, make-up, manicures, massage, osteopathy, paraffin wax treatments, peat bath, pedicures, physiotherapy, reflexology, sauna or steam cabinet, Slendertone, sunbeds, swimming pool, waxing, wax baths and yoga.

Prices include four free treatments daily (except Sundays), chosen – with the help of a consultation – from sauna, steam cabinet, massage, G5, Slendertone, osteopathy, physiotherapy and hydrotherapy; with two treatments on midweek arrival and departure days.

Ragdale Hall Health Hydro
Ragdale, Near Melton Mowbray, Leics. LE14 3PB. Tel: Rotherby (066475) 831 or 411.

About 20 minutes from the M1 motorway at junction 23, 30

minutes from the A1, and a 20-minute taxi-ride from Leicester or Loughborough main line stations.

Treatments and activities on offer include aerobics, archery, aromatherapy, assault course, Cathiodermie, chiropody, collagen treatments, eyebrow shaping, eyelash and brow dye, facials (Clarins, DeCleor, René Guinot, RoC), G5, infra-red, golf, hairdressing, jogging, make-up, manicures, massage, paraffin wax baths, pedicures, reflexology, saunas, Slendertone, solarium, squash, swimming pool, tennis, waxing, and whirlpool spa.

Prices include all meals and a selection of treatments – including massage and facials – as well as free use of many facilities.

Roundelwood
Drummond Terrace, Crieff, Tayside PH7 4AN. Tel: 0764 3806.

A castellated mansion, over 100 years old, at the foot of the Grampian mountains, overlooking the picturesque Scottish town of Crieff.

Treatments and activities on offer include arthritis and rheumatism treatment, facials, G5, gymnasium, hot blanket, hydrotherapy, massage, nursing services, physiotherapy, sauna, slimming and weight management, smoking cessation, spa bath, stress control lessons, solarium and wax baths.

Prices include all meals and all treatments except hairdressing and facials.

Shrubland Hall Health Clinic
Coddenham, Ipswich, Suffolk IP6 9QH. Tel: Ipswich (0473) 830404.

A country house, built in 1740, on one of the highest points in Suffolk, with beautiful landscaped gardens. The Hall is six miles north of Ipswich and within easy reach of the sea – the area also has one of the lowest rainfalls in England.

Treatments and activities on offer include colonic irrigation, exercise classes, hairdressing, hydrotherapy, massage, physiotherapy, postural re-education, private relaxation classes, sauna, steam cabinet, underwater massage and X-rays.

Prices include all meals and some treatments.

Stobo Castle
Peebles-shire, Scotland, EH45 8NY. Tel: 07216 249.

A castle 27 miles south of Edinburgh, with towers dominating superb wood and parkland.

Treatments and activities on offer at both include aromatherapy, acupuncture, a beauty shop, beauty demonstrations, bust treatments, Cathiodermie, ear piercing, exercise classes, faradism, facials (Clarins, René Guinot, RoC), hydrotherapy, hairdressing, a health and fitness day, Jacuzzi, massage, manicures, make-up advice, physiotherapy, paraffin wax treatments, pedicures, relaxation classes, sunbeds, seaweed baths, steam cabinets, saunas, swimming pool, underwater massage, vibro massage, water exercises, well woman programme, waxing and bleaching, and yoga.

Prices include meals and some treatments.

Tyringham Naturopathic Clinic
Newport Pagnell, Bucks. MK16 9ER. Tel: Newport Pagnell (0908) 610450.

A Georgian mansion set in rural Buckinghamshire, half way between London and Birmingham, four miles from the Newport Pagnell slip road on the M1 motorway.

Treatments and activities on offer include acupuncture, badminton, cleanse and make-up, eyelash and brow tinting, fashion shows, gymnasium, hairdressing, hydrotherapy, manicures, massage, osteopathy, pedicures, physiotherapy, sauna, spa bath, steam baths, swimming pool, tennis and table tennis, and wax baths.

Prices include all meals, consultations and therapeutic treatments.

MAN APPEAL? **Yes** – as many men as women go to health farms regularly.

PLEASURE RATING **+5**

INFRA-RED

The Facts ✍

WHAT IS IT?
Infra-red is a deep-heat lamp used for helping relax tension in the muscles. The bulb emits warm infra-red rays which penetrate deep into the muscles and joints, relieving the symptoms of arthritis and rheumatism as well as helping eliminate toxins in the body and promoting healing.

WHERE CAN YOU TRY IT?
- At health farms
- At some beauty salons

HOW MUCH SHOULD IT COST?
From around £5.

HOW OFTEN SHOULD YOU HAVE IT?
This depends on your reason for having it, and how long you use it at a time. You could, for instance, use it every day for a few minutes on a stiff joint.

HOW LONG SHOULD A TREATMENT TAKE?
From fifteen minutes to an hour. A longer treatment could cause headaches – especially if you're using the lamp on your back.
    The distance and length of the treatment is governed by your

tolerance to heat, and you should always tell the therapist if it gets too hot.

DO HAVE INFRA-RED TREATMENT:
1. if you suffer from rheumatism or arthritis.
2. if you have any aches and pains, especially backache.
3. prior to massage to heat and relax the body, ideal on neck and shoulders.

DON'T HAVE INFRA-RED TREATMENT:
1. if you have any heart complaints.
2. if you suffer from epilepsy.
3. if you have high blood pressure.
4. if you are unwell.

A Typical Infra-Red Treatment

BEFORE
• If you have fair skin you should use oil or lanolin to protect you from burns.
• If infra-red rays will be directed at your face, you should wear goggles.

DURING
1. You will be asked to undress to expose the area needing treatment, and lie on a couch. The infra-red lamp (or lamps) will then be positioned over the appropriate area (or areas) of your body, at least 6 inches/15 cm from your skin, and switched on. Some lamps glow red, others don't.
2. The therapist will then make sure you are comfortable and leave you to relax for the time allocated.
  Infra-red lamps cause a pleasant, warming sensation in the areas being treated, though you shouldn't get hot and sticky.

AFTER
• Your skin will feel very warm, and may be slightly red due to the increase in circulation – this will soon fade.

MAN APPEAL? **Yes**	PLEASURE RATING **+3**

JACUZZI

The Facts

WHAT IS IT?

A Jacuzzi is a whirlpool bath. It is, however, also a trade name, and you may find a similar pool described in a salon or health farm as a whirlpool bath, spa bath, hot tub or hydrotherapy pool.

Basically, a Jacuzzi is an enormous bath (or mini-swimming pool!) with seating at different levels around the sides, which you share with other people – though you may find one-person baths in some beauty salons. But unlike a normal bath, a Jacuzzi is fitted with a series of water jets which pummel your flesh and are said to aid slimming, help you relax, ease tension, aches and pains, and to alleviate minor ailments such as pulled muscles, sprains and strains.

The water jets, which are of varying heights and strengths, massage different parts of your body, stimulating the skin and blood supply, improving skin tone, loosening joints and relaxing muscles.

The water is at bath-water temperature (usually around 30–35°C/86–95°F), and you may even find a foaming agent being used. This not only creates attractive bubbles but can insulate the surface of the water, keeping it hot. It's almost like sharing a huge bubble bath!

Jacuzzis may be fairly recent, but water therapy – or hydrotherapy – dates back centuries. The early Romans had hot water pools where they would meet to socialise and relax, the Japanese have long soaked together in tubs, while the famous spa towns of Europe, fashionable at the end of the 19th century, made full use of the curative properties of water therapy. Today, thanks to the pioneering efforts of Italian spa bath makers Jacuzzi, you can even have a hot tub in your own home!

The advantage of having a Jacuzzi in a beauty salon or health farm is that a therapist can vary the effects of a hydrotherapy routine by adding certain substances to the water, such as essential oils (see page 21), mineral salts or herbal and floral fragrances. She can also vary the strength and type of treatment by varying the depth of water in the bath, so that different pressures can be obtained to suit the client. The deeper the water, the more pressure the compressed air produces and the stronger the massage effects.

WHERE CAN YOU TRY A WHIRLPOOL BATH?
- At larger salons and hairdressers
- At health farms
- At health clubs and leisure centres
- At some hotels and swimming pools

HOW MUCH SHOULD A SESSION COST?
Health farms, clubs etc usually have a whirlpool bath for use by clients, and don't make an extra charge for its use. In a salon a hydrotherapy treatment could cost around £5.

HOW LONG SHOULD YOU STAY IN ONE?
No longer than ten to fifteen minutes.

DO USE A JACUZZI:
1. after exercise.
2. if you need to relax.
3. if you have arthritis, muscular or rheumatic complaints.
4. as an aid to slimming. The massage jets help break down fatty deposits which accumulate around the hips, buttocks, thighs and upper arms.
5. to tone and soften your skin.

DON'T USE A JACUZZI:
1. if you've been drinking alcohol. It could make you faint.
2. if you have anything that you might pass on, such as cystitis, a verruca, thrush etc, or if you're prone to these kind of infections. Bacteria that thrive in the warm, moist conditions of spa baths can

cause skin rashes, spots and boils, thrush and cystitis – which is why it's so important for a bath and its filters to be cleaned daily.
3. if you have eczema, as your skin may get itchy and uncomfortable.

QUESTIONS YOU SHOULD ASK BEFORE USING A COMMUNAL JACUZZI
1. How often is the bath cleaned, and the filters and the quality of water checked? Certain bacteria thrive in warm water, and the Jacuzzi should be cleaned and the water changed every one to two days if you want to minimise the risk of any infection.
2. How many people can use the Jacuzzi at one time? The fewer the better (preferably two or three, and no more than eight).

A Typical Jacuzzi Session ✑

BEFORE
● Have a shower.
● Never take any oils, bubble bath or soap into the Jacuzzi.

DURING
1. You will be asked to undress (you'll wear a swimming costume in a communal Jacuzzi) and climb into the bath. Then you'll simply sit there being pleasantly pummelled by water jets until it's time to get out!
2. By changing position in a communal bath, you can find jets that will massage your back, arms etc. If at any time you start to feel faint, get out of the bath.

AFTER
● If you are wearing a swimming costume with cut-out sections, you may find it fills up rather embarrassingly with air and water during your bath. Don't be surprised if, as you clamber out, you notice you've developed a huge spare tyre and a massive bust!

RESULTS
You should feel pleasantly relaxed.

Further Information ✍

The Swimming Pool and Allied Trades Association (SPATA) have issued strict guidelines on spa pool maintenance. Their address is:

The Swimming Pool and Allied Trades Association, SPATA House, 1a Junction Road, Andover, Hants, SP10 3QT. Enquiries: 01–291 3455 (24 hours).

MAN APPEAL? Yes	PLEASURE RATING +3

LASH AND BROW TINTING

The Facts

WHAT IS IT?

Tinting is a way of temporarily darkening your lashes to give your eyes more definition, and is particularly popular with women who have very fair lashes, or dark lashes with fair tips.

You can have your eyelashes tinted most dark colours, such as black, brown and navy blue, and the main advantage is that you won't need to wear mascara any longer unless you want your lashes to look thicker, too.

Eyebrows can also be tinted, and you might choose to have this done if you've recently changed your hair colour.

The tint used is much gentler than the tint used to dye hair, because the eye area is very sensitive.

WHERE CAN YOU HAVE IT DONE?
- At beauty salons
- At some hairdressers
- At health farms and clubs

HOW MUCH SHOULD IT COST?

From around £4 for eyebrow tinting, from £5 for eyelash tinting. Salons will usually offer the two together for a slightly reduced price.

HOW OFTEN SHOULD YOU HAVE IT?

Every four to six weeks.

HOW LONG SHOULD IT TAKE?

About five to ten minutes for eyelashes; one to five minutes for eyebrows. With eyebrows the tint 'takes' much more quickly so the therapist must make sure she doesn't leave it on for too long. Having too-dark eyebrows will just give the face a hard expression!

DO HAVE YOUR LASHES OR BROWS TINTED:

1. if you've got very blonde eyelashes or fair tips on dark eyelashes.

2. if you're a redhead with gingery lashes. The difference can be quite dramatic as the chances are your lashes are very thick and lustrous.

3. if you've recently dyed your hair darker and want lashes or brows to match.

4. if you dislike wearing mascara and prefer the more natural look. Your eyelashes won't be any thicker but may appear so because of the colour.

5. if you're going on holiday and want to have good-looking lashes on the beach. Tinted lashes look very natural.

DON'T HAVE YOUR LASHES OR BROWS TINTED:

1. if you've got any kind of allergy – though the therapist could do a free patch test behind your ear 24 hours beforehand if you want to go ahead with treatment.

2. if you're prone to eye infections (eg conjunctivitis).

HOW CAN YOU TELL IF A THERAPIST IS GOOD?

1. She will be meticulous about not letting even the tiniest bit of paste touch your skin – you don't want to have your skin tinted too! (If this does happen, you'll have to wait for it to fade, which could take a few days.)

2. She will also be very careful and not let you get any tint in your eyes (if this does happen, you should immediately have an eyebath).

3. She will make sure you keep your eyes closed at all times, and check constantly that you are not feeling any discomfort. She should also stay with you throughout the treatment.

A Typical Lash Tint ✍

BEFORE
- Remove contact lenses.
- Preferably, turn up wearing no eye make-up. If you've applied lots of mascara the therapist will have to waste a great deal of time removing it before she can start the treatment!

DURING

1. The therapist will cover your clothing with a gown or towels, and will begin by removing any trace of make-up or grease from the eyes.

2. After preparing the tint, she will put vaseline on one side of two cotton-wool pads, and place a pad underneath the bottom lashes of each eye, vaseline-side down. This will protect the skin around the eyes from the tint, as you will have to keep your eyes closed throughout the treatment. The therapist must make sure that no vaseline is touching the lashes as this will prevent the hair from accepting the colour.

3. You'll then be asked to close your eyes, and the therapist will put a little vaseline on the top lid, also for protection, making sure that none touches the top lashes.

4. The therapist will make sure your eyes are still closed, then she will cover the lashes with the eyelash tint – made into a thickish paste – with an eyebrow or eyeliner brush. She must make sure that the paste is applied right down to the roots of the lashes, especially if you have fair hair.

The paste will tint the top and bottom lashes simultaneously, since the top lashes will be resting on the bottom ones when your eyes are closed. The tint will coat the underneath of the lashes too (it's not the same as applying mascara!).

5. You shouldn't be able to feel a thing, but if there is any stinging or irritation, tell the therapist immediately and she will remove the paste.

6. Once sufficient time has elapsed the therapist will remove the tint with either orange sticks tipped in cotton wool or damp cotton wool. Your eyes must remain closed.

7. The therapist will make sure that all the tint has been removed from the top lashes before she asks you to open your eyes so she can remove the tint from the bottom lashes.

AFTER
- If your eyes feel a little sensitive afterwards, avoid wearing eye make-up for a few hours.

● The tint will fade out rather than grow out. You won't get roots.

● You can, of course, use mascara on top if you like – especially to thicken lashes.

RESULTS

Your lashes will be dark, healthy and natural looking.

MAN APPEAL?   **Yes** – men do have it done, especially if they have very fair lashes.

PLEASURE RATING   **0**

MAKE-UP

The Facts

WHAT CAN A SALON OFFER YOU?

Most salons will make up your face, creating a new everyday look for you or a stunning look for a special occasion. The session will involve thorough preparation of the skin – cleansing, toning and moisturising – as well as the application of suitable cosmetics.

But while you may be happy to lie back and wait to be transformed, you may also like to know how you can achieve that look yourself. That's why many salons also offer individual make-up lessons, where you'll be shown the colours that you could wear, as well as how to apply them.

WHERE CAN YOU HAVE A MAKE-UP OR MAKE-UP LESSON?

- At most beauty salons
- At health farms and clubs
- At special make-up salons (you'll find these listed under 'Beauty Salons' in *Yellow Pages*)
- At cosmetic counters in large department stores

HOW MUCH SHOULD IT COST?

Anything from £10 upwards.

HOW OFTEN SHOULD YOU HAVE A MAKE-UP OR MAKE-UP LESSON?

Whenever you need new ideas or a new look. It's worth remembering that every season our skin, the fashion, the colours and the light change. So make-up that looks right in one season may look harsh and wrong the next.

HOW LONG SHOULD A SESSION TAKE?
This depends on what is involved. Allow about an hour.

DO HAVE A MAKE-UP OR MAKE-UP LESSON:
1. if you have been using the same shapes and colours for years. The chances are, you're looking a bit 'dated', and a good therapist will be able to introduce you to new, flattering colours, and up-to-date ways to apply them.
2. if you've never been sure how to apply make-up correctly, or the colours to use. A professional make-up or lesson is cheaper than buying a selection of expensive products which might be totally wrong for you.
3. if you fancy a new look because you don't think you're making the most of your looks; or you're not happy with the shape of one of your features (perhaps you feel your nose is too wide, or your lips too thin); or maybe you like the new season's colours but are not sure if you'll be able to wear them successfully.
4. if you are going somewhere special and want to look your best, an interview for a job, for example, or a glamorous party.
5. if you want to learn how to camouflage blemishes.
6. if you've recently changed your hair. What looked right when you had dark hair may look wrong now you're blonde.
7. if you've acquired a tan. You may need a therapist's advice on the colours that won't make you look like a painted doll!
8. if you are having photographs taken for publicity or other reasons. Studio lighting is very harsh and you may need advice on the correct amount of make-up to wear so that you don't look 'washed-out'.
9. if you are getting married. Choosing make-up colours to complement your skin and a white dress can be very tricky, and any mistakes will show up in your wedding album!

DON'T HAVE A MAKE-UP OR MAKE-UP LESSON:
1. if you have any allergy to cosmetics.

WHAT SHOULD THE THERAPIST ASK YOU?
1. About your current skin-care and make-up routine. She will be able to pinpoint any mistakes you are making.

2. What colours you like and dislike wearing. It may be that there are shades of your favourite colours which will suit you better than the ones you currently use; equally, the therapist may be able to prove that you can wear shades of the colours you've always thought wouldn't suit you.

3. If there are any products to which you are allergic.

4. What kind of look you want to achieve, for example, if it's for a special occasion such as your wedding.

WHAT SHOULD YOU ASK THE THERAPIST?

1. Whether you will be able to buy any products she uses that you particularly like.

2. If you're having a lesson, whether she will make up your face for you or whether she will make up just half and let you make up the other half, under her supervision.

3. Whether she sterilises her brushes between treatments. All good therapists will do this, to minimise any risk of infection. Sterilisers are often kept in the make-up cubicle, so you will be able to check that all brushes (particularly lip brushes) have been sterilised.

A Typical Make-up Lesson &

BEFORE

● *Do* take along the products you usually use. The therapist should show you which ones suit you and how they should be applied.

● *Do* take along the brushes you usually use so that the therapist can see what you have and advise you what to do with them.

● *Don't* have any facial treatments. Your skin will need time to rest before you apply make-up (see individual treatments in this book).

DURING

1. You'll be shown how to remove make-up, cleanse and moisturise correctly for your particular skin type. This should include advice on the products to choose – whether you should use creams or lotions, for example.

2. The therapist will then show you how to apply all the products you need, including foundation, eye make-up, powder, blusher and lipstick. She may start by asking you to select colours you think suit you, then show you whether you have chosen correctly.

She will be able to teach you 'tricks of the trade' you can use to accentuate your good features and disguise your bad ones. It's a good idea to take along a notebook and pen so you can jot down anything you think you may forget.

3. She may apply the make-up herself, explaining what she is doing at every stage; alternatively she may apply a little at each stage and ask you to continue. You're more likely to be able to recreate the make-up at home if you've had a little practice in the salon.

4. Finally, she will check that you are happy with your new look, and ask if you have any other questions. If there's anything you want her to show you again, say so now. There's nothing as infuriating as sitting at your dressing-table mirror, trying to remember how to apply certain products.

She may even give you a chart showing you how she's applied the make-up and what colours she has used, and may write down a few make-up hints for you.

AFTER

- You should have a new look that makes the most of your features.

RESULTS

By using the colours recommended and techniques you've learned, you should be able to make-up with confidence every day.

Further Information

If you want to learn make-up techniques, there are many books on the subject. Particularly good are:

Let's Make Up by Doreen Miller (Piatkus)
Make-up Made Easy by Barbara Daly (St Michael)

It's also worth knowing that the British Red Cross train volunteers to work in hospitals, teaching people how to camouflage scars and noticeable skin blemishes with the use of cosmetic creams. The volunteers work under the supervision of consultants and dermatologists, and you'll have to be referred to them by your doctor.

For more details contact:

The National Administrator, Beauty Care and Cosmetic Camouflage Service, The British Red Cross Society, 9 Grosvenor Crescent, London SW1X 7EJ. Tel: 01–235 5454.

MAN APPEAL?   **Yes** – for photography etc

PLEASURE RATING   **+3**

MANICURE

The Facts ✍

WHAT IS IT?

A manicure is a beauty treatment for the hands, concentrating on making the nails look healthy and attractive. A thorough manicure involves treating the whole nail including cuticles, shaping of the nails, massage of the hands, and colouring the nails.

Every therapist will have her own manicure procedure – the one detailed below is simply a basic example.

WHERE CAN YOU HAVE ONE?

- At special nail clinics – where you can have many different forms of manicure including nail extensions, false nails, silk-wrapped nails, to name just a few!
- At hairdressers – you can have a manicure while having your hair done
- At beauty salons – again, to save time, you could have a manicure while you're having a different treatment, but a salon shouldn't combine it with other treatments as a matter of course
- At health farms and clubs

HOW MUCH SHOULD IT COST?

Depends what's included in the treatment – expect to pay anything from £5 upwards.

HOW OFTEN SHOULD YOU HAVE ONE?
Ideally once a week if you want your nails to look good all the time. Some salons will do a revarnish if your varnish chips between manicures (this doesn't include cuticle treatment etc).

HOW LONG SHOULD IT TAKE?
About 30 minutes for a full manicure. It could take longer if you have any other specialised nail treatments, such as nail extensions.

DO HAVE A MANICURE:
1. if you have problems with your nails – breaking, flaking etc. Regular treatment will strengthen and improve the appearance of the nails.
2. if you bite your nails. It'll stop you!
3. if your nails are constantly under pressure (for example if you do a lot of typing).
4. if you want your hands to show off your jewellery. There's nothing worse than a beautiful ring on a finger topped by a grotty nail.
5. if you want to look well-groomed. Beautiful nails will add the finishing touches to your glamorous appearance. You don't want your hands to let you down!

HOW CAN YOU TELL IF A THERAPIST IS GOOD?
She will ensure that all the nail varnishes she uses are not too thick a consistency and that she doesn't apply varnish too thickly. Thick varnish will never dry properly.

WHAT MIGHT THE THERAPIST ASK YOU?:
1. If you've been unwell lately. Illness often shows in your hair and your nails. She will be able to advise you on the correct diet to improve your nails – for example, Vitamins A and B_2 are very good for nails.
2. How you usually file your nails. She will advise you what to do in future if she can see you're doing it incorrectly. For example, it's best to avoid metal files, which are very rough on the nails.
3. If you have a particular preference for length and shape of your nails, though she will advise you.

A Typical Manicure ✍

BEFORE
• If possible turn up without varnish on your nails.

DURING
1. You'll be asked to remove any rings, then the therapist will remove any nail varnish you are wearing.
2. She will start by filing the nails of one hand, using the smoother side of an emery board. She'll work from the side to the centre of each nail without 'sawing', which would encourage splitting.
   The shape of the nail will depend to some extent on the shape of the nail bed: if you have very square nails, for example, you won't want a pointed tip!
3. She will apply cuticle cream to the base of each nail on that hand using an orange stick, then she'll massage it in. Your hand will then be placed in warm soapy water – to soften the cuticles – while she repeats the same procedure on the other hand.
4. The first hand will now be taken out of the water and dried with a tissue or towel. Then the therapist will apply a creamy cuticle remover down each side of each nail wall, and using a orange stick tipped with cotton wool she will work down the nail wall and around the cuticles, in small circular movements, pushing the cuticle back. Any dead skin around the nail will be removed.
5. If you have any hang-nails – little bits of skin sticking out around the side of the nail – she will cut them off using clippers. It's not advisable to cut the cuticles.
6. That hand will rest on a towel on a cushion, topped with a tissue, while she repeats the procedure on the other hand.
7. The therapist will then apply hand cream to both hands and massage each hand in turn. This is a very pleasant and relaxing sensation, and if your manicure doesn't include a hand massage, ask for one!
8. The therapist may scrub the nails afterwards with a nail brush to ensure that all grease has been removed from the nails, particularly important if you're having a varnish. Then she'll double-check, by 'squeaking' each nail with nail polish remover, to remove all traces of oil and soap.
9. Now it's time to apply nail varnish. She will ask you to choose a nail colour, then apply first one coat of a basecoat, then two or three coats of varnish, then – depending on the nail varnish

(whether it's frosted or plain) – a topcoat. Topcoat is often only used with matt varnishes; frosted varnish doesn't need it.

10. Though it's best to let the varnish dry naturally, if you are in a hurry she may use a quick-dry spray on your nails.

AFTER
- It's also best not to blow on your nails or shake them around. Apart from the danger of bumping into something, you can also create a bubbly effect.
- Don't immerse hands into hot water for at least an hour.

Home Care ✍

- Always wear rubber gloves when washing up. Never put hands in harsh detergents.
- Eat sensibly – lots of fruit and vegetables.
- Stop biting your nails.
- Never peel off nail varnish. It will take away the top layer of the nail with it.
- Never peel off layers of nail.
- Never pull off hang-nails. Always clip them.
- Choose kind nail-polish removers: never use acetone simply on its own.
- When applying your own varnish, always use a base coat as a protection. This is particularly important if you like wearing dark coloured varnish, which can stain the nail.

Further Information ✍

Volunteers from the British Red Cross offer a hand-care service to hospital patients – both men and women. Though not professional manicurists, they are trained to offer a very welcome service which includes nail trimming and hand massage.

MAN APPEAL? **Yes**	PLEASURE RATING **+3**

MASSAGE

The Facts

WHAT IS IT?

Massage is a very beneficial beauty treatment because it will relax you, and when you feel relaxed it will show in your face – you won't have any unpleasant frown lines and your skin will look better and brighter. If you're unwell, you'll heal better if you're relaxed, too.

In England, we still tend to think of massage simply as pampering. But a regular massage can make all the difference to your well-being: if you have a massage regularly to unknot your muscles, you should be able to prevent tension accumulating.

A massage at the end of a tiring day will help you unwind. Yet, paradoxically, massage can also have an invigorating effect on you – it all depends on the movements the therapist makes, and how she makes them. It's worth remembering, though, that no two therapists will give you exactly the same massage – every therapist will have developed her own individual massage routine based on both training and experience.

In addition, some therapists may incorporate the use of electrical equipment as part of a massage (see G5, page 73). Some clients like this as they feel they're 'getting something for their money', while others find electrical massage very impersonal and prefer hand massage alone.

WHERE CAN YOU TRY A MASSAGE?
- In beauty salons
- At health farms

- At health centres that specialise in alternative medicine
- On cruise ships

NB Avoid 'massage parlours' – they might be slightly suspect!

HOW MUCH SHOULD A BASIC MASSAGE COST?
Expect to pay £6 to £10 for a back massage; £10 to £20 for a full body massage, though prices vary considerably.

HOW OFTEN SHOULD YOU HAVE ONE?
This depends – from once every six months as a treat, to every day (if you can afford it!) if you're under a great deal of stress. Provided you're in good health otherwise, there's no way you could overdo it.

It's more beneficial to have a course of treatments, but a good therapist should never try to sell you a course. Obviously, it depends whether you simply fancy the occasional treat, or are feeling down, under stress or tense, in which case it's better to have a treatment once a week or fortnight.

If you have several treatments, a therapist will be able to ease out any tension that has accumulated, and the effects will be more long-lasting than a one-off treatment.

HOW LONG SHOULD IT TAKE?
A back massage would take about half an hour, a body massage about one to one and a half hours. A face massage may also be included in your treatment, this is not the same as a facial as it simply relaxes the tension in the face. A face and back massage are also often included as part of a facial, because if you have tension in your neck and back, it shows in your face!

DO TRY A BACK OR BODY MASSAGE:
1. if your job is very demanding and you're under a lot of pressure.
2. if you've been under stress or strain for whatever reason.
3. if you sit hunched over a desk or typewriter, or drive for long periods, and can feel the effects across your neck and back.
4. if you have period pains. A stomach massage can be unbelievably relaxing if you feel comfortable with the therapist.
5. as a gentle warm-up before embarking on exercise (remember the runner in *Chariots of Fire* who had a massage before he ran?). If the therapist does the movements in an energetic way, so that you don't fall asleep, you'll be relaxed but energised and raring to go.

DON'T TRY MASSAGE:
1. if you have anything medically wrong with you – even a temperature.
2. if you have a thrombosis.
3. if you've recently had a heart attack or stroke.
4. if you have an open wound.

AND CHECK WITH YOUR DOCTOR FIRST:
1. if you have any heart problems – though some cardiologists feel that massage can be beneficial as it lowers the blood pressure.
2. if you have cancer.

HOW CAN YOU TELL IF A THERAPIST IS TRAINED?
Massage is always included as part of a beauty therapist's training, though different courses teach different amounts of anatomy and physiology. If your therapist displays a diploma from a beauty school or college you can be certain she has been taught massage.

There are many schools around the country which teach just massage but, unfortunately, there is no real national licensing of massage. An inexperienced therapist could damage the connective tissue which could eventually damage the firmness and tone of your skin, so if you are looking for a therapist the best way is by recommendation. Ask the therapist how he or she trained, how long the training was, how practised they are. And make your decision based on their answers and your observation of how professional they seem.

One of the following bodies should also be able to recommend a good therapist:

BABTAC (see page 11)

or

The International Federation of Health and Beauty Therapists, 109 Felpham Road, Felpham, West Sussex PO22 7PW. Tel: 0243 860339.

The latter is also the address and phone number of The International Sports Therapy Council.

You may feel tense the first time you have a massage – you don't know what to expect, and you may not know the salon or therapist – so it's up to the therapist to establish some kind of rapport with you. As a general rule, if you like a therapist and keep going to her, you will be able to build up a comfortable relationship. Bear in mind, too, that the therapist will find it easier to massage you the next time, too.

So to find out whether you've got a good therapist, ask yourself:

- Do I like the treatment?
- Does it make me feel better?
- Do I like the person?
- Do I feel confident in her hands?
- Do I think she is going to help me get better?
- Do I feel relaxed?

If you answer 'no' to any of these questions, go elsewhere!

Massage, like most treatments, is a two-way thing. You shouldn't think of yourself simply as an inert being who's having a treatment, but as *part* of the treatment.

But you shouldn't find a 'bad' therapist – people trained to do massage tend to enjoy their work!

SHOULD YOU CHOOSE A MASSEUR OR MASSEUSE?

On the whole, women generally prefer being massaged by women, simply because they feel they'll be less embarrassed. So if you're at a health farm, say, and are allocated a masseur, speak up if you'd rather have a woman!

But it doesn't follow that a man will give a stronger massage than a woman. Some can be very gentle, just as some women can give a massage that's almost too firm.

Sometimes, though, you will be choosing a therapist because of what he or she is offering – for example, many therapists who specialise in sports massage are men.

WHAT SHOULD THE THERAPIST ASK YOU?

1. Is there anything medically wrong with you?
2. Do you have varicose veins? In which case, the therapist will avoid massaging your legs in case she sends up a clot.
3. Are you pregnant?
4. Do you have a heart problem or pacemaker?
5. What relaxes you (back massage, face and temple massage, foot massage)?

WHAT SHOULD YOU TELL THE THERAPIST?

1. What you want from the treatment (are you tired, under stress, achey?) If you are lacking in energy it can be because your muscles are too tight.
2. Whether you want to feel pleasantly relaxed or raring to go.

A Typical Back Massage Session ✍

BEFORE

- Even with a back massage, you will probably end up with oil in the hairline, so if your hair is clean and you want to keep it that way, warn the therapist.
- *Do* have a steam bath, sauna or steam cabinet. It'll make it easier for the therapist to massage you: she'll be able to 'get in deeper' because the muscles are already relaxed. It will therefore be more effective.
- *Do* try some exercise, followed by a shower. When you do strenuous exercise you release lactic acids into the surrounding muscles, and one of the reasons people get stiff when they take up exercise is because it takes a while for the lymphatic system to get those pumped up to the lymph nodes. Massage can get rid of the unpleasant effects of exercise.
- With a face massage, you will have to remove contact lenses, and take off necklaces. If you're having the ears massaged (which is very pleasant), take off your earrings. And if you're worried about getting rings oily, take those off too.
- *Don't* eat a large meal directly before having your stomach massaged.

DURING

1. First of all you'll be asked to undress. How much you take off should be up to you – wear whatever makes you feel most relaxed. But it's best to take off anything tight, trousers, for example.

It's probably comfier to take off your bra, but if you prefer to keep it on the therapist can easily slip the straps down when she massages your neck, and undo your bra when working on your back.

The same goes for your pants – she can pull them down slightly if necessary.

A therapist will cover up with towels all the areas she is not working on, so you should always feel warm and comfortable.

2. You'll then be asked to lie face down on a couch in a warm, darkened room (perhaps with some gentle background music to get you in the mood), and you'll be covered in blankets. You'll usually be asked to lie in whichever position you feel most comfortable, perhaps with your head on both hands, or with your arms loosely bent and hands at shoulder level, or hanging loosely at your sides perhaps. Some people lie with their head on one side – if you do, remember to move it at some point otherwise you'll end up with a crick in your neck.

If you begin to feel uncomfortable during the treatment, you may need padding – perhaps a pillow under your chest. So tell the therapist.

3. The therapist will then choose a suitable massage oil. It's best to massage with oils as the hands can slide more easily. In addition, if essential oils are used, they are beneficial to the skin, and the aromas will help you relax.

If you know you're allergic to any oil, check that the therapist is using essential oils rather than paraffin, mineral or baby oil. It's most unlikely that you will be allergic to essential oils.

The most soothing oils include jasmine, rose, sandalwood and lavender. If you don't like the aroma of a particular oil, tell the therapist. If she uses it, you won't be able to relax, and that will defeat the object!

4. Different massage schools teach different patterns of strokes; a pattern ensures that a therapist doesn't miss any movement out. The movements, too, may vary, but the four basic ones are stroking, kneading, pressures and slapping, which can all be done in a variety of ways.

A massage will begin with soothing, stroking movements, so that you can get used to the therapist's hands. Stroking is a linking and calming movement. Kneading and pressures are much deeper – the therapist is working on the muscles and deep tissue – and the same applies to friction or pressures. Slapping – soft, brisk blows – will wake and stimulate you.

The therapist will be able to feel your tension, where the knots are, and will work on them. Large knots may need a large amount of kneading, which can be slightly uncomfortable at first, but shouldn't actually hurt.

Some therapists use hacking, pounding and clapping, which are energising movements, and will stimulate rather than send you to sleep. With clapping, the therapist will use cupped hands which drop loosely on to your body and then spring up again. It's very pleasant but makes a very loud, hollow clapping sound which may reverberate around the room – not so bad if you're in a separate treatment room, but if you're in a cubicle it may be a bit embarrassing. Remember, though, that everyone sounds as noisy, and it's no reflection on the amount of fat you have distributed around your body!

5. A movement might hurt if you have fluid retention, an oedema of any sort. So you should always say if anything hurts or is uncomfortable, or if you don't like it. The idea of massage is to make you better!

You'll usually find that one side of your body is more sensitive than the other.

6. You should find yourself in a relaxed state half-way towards sleep. You might want to talk a little to the therapist at first, to establish a relationship, but then it's good to lie back, enjoy the massage and really concentrate on the sensations.

7. At the end of a massage, the therapist will lay her hands briefly at the base of your spine. You'll feel warm and relaxed – and probably ready to fall asleep! She'll then cover your back and leave you until you are ready to get up.

AFTER

• It's better if you can organise your day so that directly after a relaxing massage you can do things at a slower pace. It's a pity if you then get into your car and get stuck in a traffic jam!

Do low-key things: if you can spare the time, lie down for five to ten minutes to enjoy the effects of the massage. At a health farm, for instance, you wouldn't want to go and do an aerobics class directly after a massage. But you might do a yoga class, or go for a gentle swim.

• Occasionally, a therapist might be over-enthusiastic and bruise you by massaging too strongly, especially if you're very tense. This doesn't necessarily mean you've got a bad therapist, simply that the strength was wrong for you. What happened – especially if it was your first time – was that the therapist could not judge how you would react. Everyone reacts differently – you can't tell just by looking at someone, for instance, whether they like a soft or a hard massage. Your size doesn't come into it either.

• If, when you get up from a massage, you feel stiff, it probably means your body needed padding somewhere. Some people need padding under their stomach (if they have a sway back) or a pillow under the chest or forehead.

RESULTS

The effects of a massage should be immediate. When you've had a massage your circulation will look better, your face will glow (even if you have a body massage), and you will look and feel wonderfully relaxed. Your face might be a bit pinker than usual, but it will soon return to normal.

Massage will slow you down a bit, and you'll feel as if you're floating along. And the effects can be long-lasting – some people claim the feelings of well-being stay with them as long as a week.

Further Information ✍

If you want to teach yourself some massage techniques – to practise on yourself or your friends, there are a number of books you'll find helpful. These include:

Your Health and Beauty Book by Clare Maxwell-Hudson (Macdonald)
The Face and Body Book, edited by Miriam Stoppard (Windward)
The Alternative Health Guide by Brian Inglis and Ruth West (Michael Joseph)

MAN APPEAL?   **Yes** – it's very popular with men.

PLEASURE RATING   **+5**

MUD TREATMENTS

The Facts

WHAT ARE THEY?

Mud – though not the kind you'll find in your garden! – has been found to ease all sorts of health problems as well as promote healthy skin, which is why you'll find a variety of mud treatments being offered in salons.

You can try everything from a clay mask to deep-cleanse the skin, to a hot mud pack for relieving aching and stiff joints. The kinds of mud on offer include volcanic mud from the lakes of Padua in Italy, mineral-rich Dead Sea mud, glorious mud from the Techirghiol Lake near the Black Sea, Neydharting Moor from Austria, and even rotting vegetation from the banks of the Danube (fortunately, not as unpleasant as it sounds)!

WHERE CAN YOU TRY ONE?

- At many beauty salons
- At health farms

HOW MUCH SHOULD A TREATMENT COST?

Depends on the treatment. Le Moor, for example, would cost around £15 to £20 for a facial treatment, £20 to £30 for a body treatment; Parafango costs from £8 for spot treatment (knees, elbows etc) to around £15 for a large area such as hips and thighs.

HOW OFTEN SHOULD YOU HAVE A TREATMENT?

Depends on the treatment. You could have a Le Moor body

treatment, for example, once a week to begin with, or a Parafango treatment once a day for a week to see any marked improvement in a condition.

HOW LONG SHOULD A TREATMENT TAKE?
Depends on the treatment. A Le Moor body treatment takes about one and a half hours; Parafango takes about fifteen minutes.

DO HAVE A MUD TREATMENT:
1. if you have eczema or psoriasis. Dead Sea mud contains potasssium, magnesium and bromine, and has been found to give relief.
2. if you have rheumatism or aching joints. Try Dead Sea mud, Parafango (see page 116) or Neydharting Moor.
3. if you have acne. Try Le Moor masks (see below), or Dea Sea mud.
4. to pep up a tired or aching system. Neydharting Moor can improve circulation.
5. to rehydrate the skin. Try Le Moor masks.

DON'T TRY CERTAIN MUD TREATMENTS:
1. (eg masks) if you have highly sensitive skin.
2. (eg Parafango) if you have very fair skin. It could be too hot for you, and you could end up red and blotchy, rather like the effect you get if you've been sitting in front of an electric fire.
3. (eg Parafango) if you are one of the people who shouldn't try heat treatments (see Sauna, page 135), if you have heart problems, epilepsy etc, for example.

A Typical Le Moor Facial Mask ✐

WHAT IS LE MOOR?
The 'black mask' is a vegetal product, deriving from rotting vegetation from the banks of the Danube. It is over 30,000 years old and its properties are said to include rehydration of the skin as well as the relief of acne. It is suitable for all kinds of skin, and can also be used as a body treatment.

BEFORE
● *Don't* have a treatment directly before a special occasion. Like any other facial, impurities may come to the surface of your skin!

DURING

1. You will be asked to take off your shirt and lie on a couch as for other facials. The therapist would then start by cleansing the skin.

2. She will now use a facial scrub to gently remove the top layer of dead skin so that the properties of the mask can be properly absorbed. Then she will spray your face with a special water that is derived from the black mask. It's clear, pleasant, and will rehydrate the skin as well as making it receptive to cream.

3. You will then be given a facial massage, using an appropriate cream, before the therapist applies the black mask to your face. She'll apply it with a spatula to the most sensitive areas last, and remove it from those areas first.

4. The mask will be left on for four to six minutes. It really is black, and very creamy, and it feels warm. You should feel the skin tingling. If it becomes uncomfortable, tell the therapist immediately.

5. Finally, the mask will be removed with water.

AFTER

- *Don't* go out in the sun immediately after a treatment.
- You can wear make-up afterwards.

RESULTS

Your skin should look lighter and cleaner.

MAN APPEAL? **Yes**	PLEASURE RATING **+1**

A Typical Parafango Neck and Shoulder Treatment ✒

WHAT IS PARAFANGO?

Parafango is a hot volcanic mud from the lakes of Padua in Italy. It is mixed with a wax to make it more pliable and easier for the therapist to use. Melted down in a kind of cauldron, it is then applied to areas such as elbows, knees and backs, suffering from arthritis or aches and pains. It can also be used to give relief from tennis elbow or frozen shoulder.

DURING

1. You'll be asked to undress – you'll need to remove your bra – while the therapist prepares the Parafango. She will make sure it's not too hot for you by testing it with her own hands.

2. She will now place the 'sheet' of mud in position on a couch – it looks rather like melted chocolate – and you'll be asked to lie on top. Using towels pulled tightly across your body, the therapist will strap you tightly to the mud, to keep in the heat and to hold your body against the mud so that you get the most benefit. It is the mixture of heat and the mineral salts in the mud which help relieve aches and pains.

The mud will feel quite hot at first, but you will soon get used to the heat, and you will notice it starting to cool down after about five minutes. But the hotter you have Parafango, the better.

3. You will then be left for fifteen minutes – the time it takes for the mud to cool down.

4. The therapist will help you off the couch – the mud will still remain on the couch, not stick to your body.

AFTER
- You should feel pleasantly relaxed.
- Your body will not be stained brown!

RESULTS
After a course of treatment you should obtain temporary relief from aches and pains.

MAN APPEAL? **Yes**	PLEASURE RATING **+3**

PANTHERMAL

The Facts

WHAT IS IT?
Also called the Ionozone, this Italian machine looks like an elongated steam cabinet (see page 145) or small spaceship – some people call it the 'iron lung'! – and it will cleanse and tone the skin, and may help cellulite. You lie down in it on a slatted wooden rack, with your head poking out the top, just like in a steam cabinet.

The temperature inside the Panthermal is around 38°C/100°F, near body temperature, and the idea is that you're made to perspire at a low temperature, so that you don't have so many of the problems associated with overheating the body.

WHERE CAN YOU TRY IT?
• At certain health farms
• At a few large beauty salons and slimming clinics

HOW MUCH SHOULD IT COST?
Around £8 to £10.

HOW OFTEN SHOULD YOU HAVE IT?
Once in a while – it's refreshing. At a health farm many clients have it once a day as it doesn't put too much stress on the body since it's not *over*heating it.

HOW LONG SHOULD IT TAKE?
Around 30 minutes.

DO HAVE A PANTHERMAL:
1. as part of a slimming campaign, along with dieting, but remember that, like other steam treatments, you will only lose water with a Panthermal, and this will be regained as soon as you have a drink.
2. if you are trying to get rid of cellulite.
3. as a once-in-a-while pick-me-up for your skin.
4. to help you relax.
5. to soothe aching muscles and joints.

DON'T HAVE A PANTHERMAL:
1. if you have any heart problems.
2. if you have any respiratory problems, such as bronchitis or asthma.
3. if you suffer from epilepsy.
4. if you have acute eczema or any other flaking skin complaint.
5. if you suffer from diabetes.
6. if you have any medical condition or infectious disease.
7. if you have high or low blood pressure.
8. if you are pregnant.
9. if you are claustrophobic, although the therapist will stay with you all the time, so you *could* try it.
10. if you're not very nimble, as the machine is quite tricky to get into!

A Typical Panthermal Treatment ✍

DURING
1. You will be asked to climb into the cabinet and lie on the wooden slatted rack. This can be quite tricky as the machine is off the ground, at a fairly awkward angle. The rack is, however, much more comfortable than it looks. The front of the cabinet is then closed.
2. The dome will fill up with vapour which comes from underneath the rack on which you are lying. This will produce profuse sweating of the body, which will open the pores. The temperature of the vapour will, however, still be very low.

3. After a while, the dome will then fill up with oxygen. This works on the skin and makes it look lovely and fresh.

4. Then a blend of essential oils – specially selected for your particular skin – is sprayed into the dome, and goes all over the body. Because your skin is warm the oil blend will be more easily absorbed.

5. The treatment finishes with a cool needle-jet shower which will get the circulation going. It will actually feel stone cold because by this time your body will be very warm.

AFTER
- To get the most out of this treatment, it would be best to have a short rest afterwards.

RESULTS
You should feel lovely and relaxed after a Panthermal, and your skin should look smooth and glowing.

MAN APPEAL? Yes	PLEASURE RATING +2

PARAFFIN WAX

The Facts

WHAT IS IT?
Paraffin wax is a localised heat treatment for different parts of the body – usually the hands and feet – but it can also be given as a full-length bath. It softens and cleanses the skin, and stimulates the circulation. If you're having a full paraffin bath, it will make you perspire – which will help rid the body of waste products – and may help speed up skin regeneration.

The temperature of the wax is controlled so that it is sufficiently runny but not too hot. It should be between 45–47°C/110–120°F.

WHERE CAN YOU HAVE IT?
- At most beauty salons
- At health farms and clubs
- At slimming clinics

HOW MUCH WILL IT COST?
From around £5 for feet or hands, £20 for the whole body.

HOW OFTEN SHOULD YOU HAVE IT?
Every one to six weeks.

HOW LONG WILL A TREATMENT TAKE?
About fifteen to twenty minutes on limbs, fifteen to twenty minutes on the whole body.

DO HAVE A PARAFFIN WAX TREATMENT:

1. on the hands if they are very dry.
2. on the feet if you've been standing on your feet all day long, or suffer from hard skin. (You could have a treatment alongside a pedicure, the ultimate in luxury!)
3. if you have arthritis or stiff joints.
4. if you want to soften skin on the body.
5. in conjunction with other slimming treatments – but remember that any weight loss will be regained immediately the minute you have a drink, since you are only losing water from your body.
6. to get your skin in good condition for a holiday.

DON'T HAVE A PARAFFIN WAX:

1. if you have any acute skin disorder.
2. for a body treatment if you are claustrophobic.
3. if you have any heart complaint.
4. if you suffer from diabetes.
5. if you suffer from epilepsy.
6. if you're under fifteen or over sixty.
7. for a body treatment if you are pregnant.

A Typical Foot Paraffin Wax ✑

BEFORE
- *Don't* have any other heat treatment, eg sauna or steam bath.
- *Don't* have a leg wax.
- *Don't* use cream depilatories.

DURING

1. First of all, you'll be asked to remove your tights, skirt or dress and slip. Then you'll be asked to sit on a chair or lie on a couch, and polythene will be placed on top of a towel – to catch any dripping wax – on the floor or under your legs.
2. The paraffin wax may be heated in a separate container, and the therapist will keep refilling a metal or enamel bowl with enough wax to work with. She will check on her own hand that the wax is at the correct temperature for application, then she will place your foot inside the bowl and ladle over the wax. Alternatively, she may use a specially designed thermostatically-controlled plunge bath, in which you'll be asked to place your feet.

The wax used has a low melting point so that when you remove your feet the wax will solidify quickly.

3. Several coats of wax will be applied to your feet, after which they will be wrapped in waxproof paper, covered with a towel and left for the required amount of time.

4. At the end of the treatment, the therapist will peel off the wax – this won't hurt a bit! – and may hold your feet under cold running water for a minute or so.

AFTER
● Your feet should feel comfortable and smooth.

RESULTS
Regular treatment should give temporary relief from painful joints.

MAN APPEAL? **Yes**	PLEASURE RATING+3

PEDICURE

The Facts

WHAT IS IT?

Many of us still regard a pedicure as a luxury, probably because our feet are hidden for most of the year in shoes and boots. But feet deserve plenty of attention because, throughout a lifetime, they need to carry us the equivalent of four times round the world!

A pedicure is much more than simply a manicure of the feet. A regular pedicure will help prevent problems such as corns, callouses (hard skin) and ingrown toe-nails, while a therapist can offer invaluable advice about correct footcare and footwear. Badly fitting shoes and inattention to hygiene are to blame for most foot problems!

WHERE CAN YOU HAVE IT DONE?

- At beauty salons
- At health farms
- At Scholl foot clinics. There are around sixty in major cities in the UK, which also sell a wide range of footcare products.

HOW MUCH SHOULD IT COST?

Depends on what is included in the treatment (for example, paraffin wax treatment or massage), and the condition of the feet. A basic pedicure starts at around £10, while more comprehensive treatments can cost around £20.

HOW OFTEN SHOULD YOU HAVE ONE?

- As often as you go to the dentist! Every six to twelve months as a preventative measure if your feet are in good condition; ideally at the change of season – when the weather gets warmer and you start to wear open sandals, and at the end of the summer when you will be going into heavy shoes and boots.
- Every four to six weeks at first if you are beginning to develop corns.
- Every two to four months if you have 'problem feet'.

HOW LONG SHOULD IT TAKE?
Up to an hour.

DO HAVE A PEDICURE:

1. if you are pregnant. Pregnant women tend to put extra pressure on the balls of their feet and their toes and could develop problems. In addition, because of all the extra weight you are putting on in a very short amount of time, you may start getting aches and pains in your heels, ankles and lower leg muscles – and a pedicure is very soothing.

2. if you have recently put on weight (see above).

3. six weeks before a holiday to get your feet in good condition, and leave you time for a further treatment if necessary.

4. if you have just returned from a holiday and have dry skin on your feet.

5. if there's been a long spell of hot weather. Many women from hot countries have a pedicure every two to three weeks whether they have problems or not.

6. if your job involves a great deal of standing.

7. after an exhausting shopping session – pavements can be very hard on the feet!

DON'T HAVE A PEDICURE:

1. if you have severe callouses or an inflamed ingrown toe-nail – it's best to consult a chiropodist instead.

2. if you have a verruca or athlete's foot, or anything contagious.

3. if you suffer from diabetes.

4. if you suffer from poor circulation.

5. if you are taking steroids or anti-coagulants.

6. if a condition has turned septic.

FOOT NOTES

Foot problems	Causes	Remedies
Pain in the heel	Your age. As you reach your fifties the natural padding under your feet wears thin and the heel bone has to cope with extra pressure	Invest in insoles or a heel cushion
Burning sensation under balls of feet	Metatarsal arch or arches have collapsed, or may be due to callouses (see below)	Wear flatter shoes, or arch supports in shoes. These can be fitted for you at Scholl centres and will support feet
Corns – on the tips of toes and between them	Friction, pressure and perspiration	Check seams of tights and shoes for cause; wear lower heels and less pointed toes; and dust between toes with foot powder to absorb perspiration (or wear a toe separator)
Callouses (ie hard skin)	Too-high heels, affecting posture and putting pressure on balls of feet	Wear more sensible footwear or at least insoles for cushioning
Bunions	Usually hereditary, but triggered off by badly-fitting tights or too-short or too-pointed shoes	Wear generously cut shoes; avoid high heels. Try bunion pads or shields
Blisters	Friction	Use protective padding. Don't pierce blister, but it if breaks on its own, wash it with antiseptic solution and cover with sterile bandage during day
Ingrown toe-nails	Injury or badly fitting tights or shoes. Or incorrect cutting of nails – toe-nails should be cut straight across, never shaped	See a chiropodist

A Typical Scholl Pedicure ✍

BEFORE
- The therapist should ask whether you have any allergies. If you are allergic to lanolin, for instance, the therapist would have to avoid using sticking plaster, which might irritate the skin.
- Tell the therapist if you have any particular problems, so she can investigate the cause. If, for example, corns are beginning to form, it could simply be due to the way your tights fit – the seam may be rubbing the skin. Or your shoes might be the culprit – they may be too tight, or the lining may be rubbing against a joint.
- *Do* remove any nail varnish from toes.

DURING
1. First of all you'll be asked to remove your shoes and tights (you may want to remove your skirt, too, to avoid creasing). Then you'll sit upright on a comfortable lounger, with your feet on a towel on the therapist's lap.

The therapist will start by soaking your feet in a cream footbath to soften the skin and nails while she talks to you about footcare and discusses any problems. She'll then dry your feet thoroughly, paying attention to between the toes.
2. Now she will cleanse and tone the skin with surgical alcohol to make sure your feet are clean and sterile, with no cream left on them.
3. The therapist will then clip your toe-nails straight across (shaping at the sides encourages ingrown toe-nails). A clipper is better than scissors because nails are made up of hundreds of different layers, glued together, and a clipper cuts through them all at once, whereas scissors can split the nail.
4. Now she will bevel the nails with a metal file to seal the layers together before cleaning away the debris from around the nails with 10 volume hydrogen peroxide.

Toe-nails tend to be stronger than fingernails, but if you have particularly hard toe-nails there's usually an explanation: perhaps you wore shoes that were too small when you were a child, which can cause nails to thicken; or maybe you've had some kind of accident – you've dropped something on your toe-nails, or been trodden on by a horse!

On the other hand, somebody with rheumatoid arthritis would have very thin, brittle nails, while some illnesses result in a colour change in the nails.
5. Using a hoofed orange stick, in tiny circular movements, the therapist will work around the nails and cuticles with a condi-

tioning cuticle cream to remove any of the little dead bits of skin that get glued on to the nail.

6. After checking for any corns and callouses – and treating them if necessary – the therapist will now use a little sanding disc to remove the surface layer of dead skin from underneath your feet and leave them beautifully smooth.

This is the only part of the treatment that may tickle slightly – worth remembering if you've never tried a pedicure because you've got very sensitive feet and always though you might get a fit of the giggles!

She will finish this part of the treatment by applying moisturising cream.

7. She will now massage your feet, which is good for your circulation as well as being very pleasant and relaxing.

8. Time for the finishing touches. First she will ask you to choose the colour of nail varnish you would like, and after removing any remaining grease from the nails she'll apply first a basecoat, then two layers of varnish, then a protective nail hardener; then she'll use a menthol-based conditioning spray to cool and refresh the feet; and finally she will spray your feet with a fine dusting powder.

AFTER
● Your feet will feel light and comfortable, and you'll feel very relaxed.
● If you can, rest for a short while to make the most of the treatment.

RESULTS
Your feet will look good, and should stay in good condition.

Home Care ✍

You should give yourself a pedicure every ten to fourteen days to keep them in good condition. Many beauty books offer advice on giving yourself a pedicure – your therapist will also be able to advise you. But here are some useful guidelines:
● When pushing back cuticles, never poke or push too hard, especially around the half-moon area. Here, the nail cells are still very soft and you can damage the nail as it grows.
● Never cut your toe-nail cuticles – soak them for about ten minutes and then just push them back.

● It's best to leave your nails free of varnish for about four months of the year – say in winter, when they're not on show – otherwise they start to stain. This can damage them and make them brittle and weak.

Also, if you wear nail varnish constantly you may pick up a fungus infection, similar to athlete's foot, underneath the nail.

● It's always worth carrying a small cooling foot spray with you – Scholl do a useful handbag-sized one – to refresh the feet and prevent them from swelling, particularly if you work in a shop with nylon carpets, or your shoes are synthetic-lined.

● Always wear dusting powder between your toes if you stand all day long. It acts as a dry lubricant and stops your toes from rubbing against each other. Choose unperfumed powder, because the skin in this area is very sensitive and may get irritated by perfume.

● If you like to wear your toe-nails slightly longer in summer, when you're wearing open sandals, remember that nails should never come more than a couple of millimetres above the tip of the toes. Remember, too, that long nails will take up a lot of extra room in your shoes.

● Make sure that after having a bath you always dry in between toes properly – this will prevent infections such as athlete's foot.

Further Information ✍

For serious foot problems, always consult a chiropodist. You can find chiropodists listed in the *Yellow Pages*, under 'Chiropodists', and the letters MChS after the name mean that a chiropodist is a member of the Society of Chiropodists.

MAN APPEAL? **Yes** – almost as many men have pedicures as women.

PLEASURE RATING **+4**

REFLEXOLOGY

The Facts

WHAT IS IT?

Reflexology is an unusual and wonderfully relaxing foot massage which originated in China over 4,000 years ago. Though it is really an alternative health treatment rather than a beauty treatment, it is becoming very popular and common in beauty salons, often practised alongside aromatherapy.

You only have to consider that when your feet are in agony it shows on your face, so it follows that if your feet have been soothed, and are lovely and light, you'll feel terrific!

But reflexology is also a healing treatment. Using her fingertips, a therapist will make a series of pressing movements around your feet, stimulating reflexes which are linked to every part of your body. The result of this is that toxins are released, circulation is improved, organ and gland functions are improved, and your whole body – and your mind – will be relaxed. And it can relieve all kinds of painful and disabling conditions from migraine headaches to arthritis.

WHERE CAN YOU TRY IT?

- At many beauty salons
- At health farms and clubs
- At alternative health centres

HOW MUCH SHOULD IT COST?

Around £15.

HOW OFTEN SHOULD YOU HAVE IT?

Once a week for three weeks, then once a month or six weeks. This does, however, depend on the individual and the problems you want corrected. You shouldn't have treatments more often than every three days.

HOW LONG SHOULD A SESSION TAKE?

Unless you have very sensitive feet, around 40 minutes (20 minutes on each foot). But the larger the foot, the longer the treatment will take!

DO HAVE REFLEXOLOGY:

1. if you suffer from tension.
2. if you have arthritis. It can relieve pain and release stiff joints.
3. whatever your age. It's a very gentle treatment, and elderly people find it particularly beneficial.

DON'T HAVE REFLEXOLOGY:

1. if you're under heavy sedation or medication.
2. if you've recently had internal surgery.
3. if you're pregnant. If you're feeling well, and you've enjoyed reflexology before, you could have a short session of gentle massage, but do check with your doctor first.
4. during your period. You could feel some discomfort and the treatment could prolong bleeding.
5. if you suffer from diabetes.
6. if you have athlete's foot or a verruca.
7. if you have shingles.
8. if you have any heart problems.
9. if you're frightened of the treatment.
10. if you have puffy ankles.

HOW CAN YOU TELL IF A THERAPIST IS GOOD?

1. You don't have to be a beauty therapist to practise reflexology, but a good reflexologist is one who is experienced: the longer she has been doing it, the stronger her fingers and the easier it will be for her to find and work on the nerve endings.
2. She should try to get you into a pleasant, relaxed state – you might even like to doze off during the treatment, or, if it's your first treatment, at least shut your eyes. She should certainly never chat about other subjects, or let you dwell on your own problems.
3. She must also have very short, clipped nails, filed smoothly.

Reflexology is carried out with the ball of the fingers and you don't want her to scratch you.

4. A good therapist will also point out areas on the hands and feet on which you could work yourself at home. For example, if you're prone to seasickness she should be able to show you how to alleviate this by working on the solar plexus nerve endings on your hands.

REFLEXOLOGY AND BABIES

How many times have you done 'this little piggy went to market . . .' on a tiny baby? Well, you've been using reflexology!

Each time you've rotated a tiny toe you've been relaxing part of the baby's body. Rotating that big toe, for instance, relaxes the neck.

A Typical Reflexology Treatment ✍

BEFORE
- *Don't* have a treatment directly after a meal – you might feel slightly queasy, and the results might not be particularly beneficial – or if you are hungry.

DURING
1. You'll be asked to remove your shoes and tights and will sit, keeping the spine straight, in a firm and comfortable chair in a darkened room, possibly with relaxing music playing in the background. The therapist will then start by checking for any foot complaint before giving you a footbath containing an aromatherapy oil, which is both antiseptic and pleasant-smelling, to help you relax.

2. She'll now dry your feet and start gently with your left foot – the left side of your body is the 'receiving' part, and more toxins accumulate there. She will rotate your ankle, and see whether you are relaxed – she will be able to feel any tension in your body.

Reflexology is carried out on dry feet, so the therapist can reach all the nerve endings, each of which is connected to certain areas of the body.

3. With the cushiony ball of her thumb she will then make a series of quick pressing movements in a certain sequence around your foot – the movement of her thumb is rather like a crawling caterpillar. Every pressure point – they're about ¹⁄₁₆ inch/ (1.5 mm) apart – corresponds to, or is linked to, a particular organ or gland in the body.

As she goes, she will be able to spot 'problem' areas – and so will you: she'll feel a bit of 'crunching' under her fingertip and you'll feel as though she's sticking her fingernail into you!

Tenderness doesn't, however, mean that the particular organ is sick: it simply indicates tension in that particular area.

4. She will work on your whole body, not try to diagnose and work on one bit. But she'll concentrate on massaging those problem areas: the pressure she applies breaks down congestion there so that the toxins that have built up can be eliminated via the bloodstream, urine or sweat glands.

It's not always a tender spot in the body that's causing the problem. The body is split up into zones that are used for reflexology, and if something shows up in one part of that zone, the problem could be anywhere in that zone.

You may feel tingling, either in the part the therapist is working on, or anywhere else in the body.

5. She'll then repeat the procedure with the right foot – the 'giving' side of your body. Treatment may be less effective if the therapist starts with this foot.

6. Finally, she will ask you to take a couple of deep breaths, or she may use a relaxation technique to help you forget any discomfort you may have felt during the treatment.

AFTER
- You'll feel very relaxed so don't immediately jump up and do something strenous. It's best if you can lie down, or even nap, for a while.

A CORNY STORY

A chiropodist who took a course in reflexology realised that the hard skin from which many of his patients suffered tended to develop over one particular stress area – the thyroid area.

So now, instead of cuttting the hard skin away, he uses reflexology on the area and reports that the hard skin is less likely to recur . . .

RESULTS

After a series of treatments you should obtain relief from all kinds of problems, from stress-related conditions such as migraine, skin rashes, menstrual problems and digestive disorders, to asthma.

Reflexology will also improve circulation, tone up the body and promote a feeling of well-being.

Further Information ✑

The following organisation can supply a list of qualified therapists in Britain and Europe.

The International Institute of Reflexology, PO Box 34, Harlow, Essex, CM17 0LT.

Reflexology is also featured in a number of good books on alternative medicine. These include:

The Alternative Health Guide by Brian Inglis and Ruth West (Michael Joseph)
Reflexology by Anna Kaye and Don C. Matchan (Thorsons)
Techniques of Foot Massage by Kaye Matchan (Thorsons)
Practical Aromatherapy by Shirley Price (Thorsons)

MAN APPEAL?   **Yes** – especially to get rid of tensions at the end of the day.

PLEASURE RATING   **+3**

Sauna

The Facts

WHAT IS IT?
A sauna is a small wooden room or cabin in which coals are burned to create a hot, dry atmosphere, and the temperature can be anything up to 80°C/176°F. The heat of a sauna can be very relaxing, and soothing for aching joints. This kind of dry heat is also one of the best ways to deep-cleanse the skin, and can even inhibit the growth of viruses and infections. The Finns believe that it makes joints supple and soothes and refreshes the mind; they are said to follow a sauna with a massage with birch twigs to stimulate circulation, and a roll in the snow!

WHERE CAN YOU TRY IT?
- At some beauty salons
- At health farms and clubs
- At some leisure centres
NB Avoid 'unisex saunas' which might be slightly suspect!

HOW MUCH SHOULD IT COST?
At many health farms and clubs use of the sauna is included in the price; if not, you might pay anything from £5.

HOW OFTEN SHOULD YOU HAVE A SAUNA?
Two or three times a week.

HOW LONG SHOULD YOU STAY IN ONE?
To start with, five minutes. As you get used to the heat you can

build up your time to around twenty minutes, but remember it's dangerous to subject your body to intense heat for long periods.
    You will probably feel when you've had enough.

DO HAVE A SAUNA:
1. to cleanse your skin. If you have one regularly you'll certainly notice an improvement in its condition.
2. in conjunction with massage and diet to speed up an anti-cellulite programme. But remember that the only thing you'll lose from your body during a sauna is water – not fat – so it has no effect on its own as a slimming treatment.
3. before a massage.

DON'T HAVE A SAUNA:
1. if you have any serious respiratory problems such as bronchitis or asthma.
2. if you have any heart complaint.
3. if you have acute eczema or any other flaking skin complaint (your skin may become itchy and uncomfortable due to the heat).
4. if you suffer from epilepsy.
5. if you are diabetic.
6. if you have symptoms of any illness or feel generally unwell.
7. if you have high or low blood pressure.
8. if you have an infectious disease.
9. if you suffer from thrombosis.
10. if you are pregnant.
11. if you suffer from claustrophobia.
12. if you have severe inflammation of the eyes or nose.

QUESTIONS YOU SHOULD ASK:
Is the sauna single-sex or mixed?

A Typical Sauna Session ✑

BEFORE
● *Don't* have a sauna directly after a strenuous bout of exercise – your body will already be heated up.
● *Do* have a warm shower before going into a sauna – it will open your pores, relax your muscles, and can help speed up the sweating process.
● *Do* remove all jewellery. The metal can heat up and burn the skin.

DURING

1. You'll undress. It's best to wear nothing except a towel, though there's nothing to stop you wearing a swimming costume or bikini bottom if you think you may be embarrassed. Then you'll go into the sauna and find somewhere to sit. There will be slatted wooden benches around the room, possibly at different levels – the higher you sit, the hotter the temperature.

2. The sauna shouldn't be unbearably hot, but after only a short while you'll find yourself perspiring. Cold water may be thrown on to the coals from time to time to increase the heat and moisture in the room: this is said to be good for the upper respiratory tract and may relieve symptoms of arthritis and certain skin diseases.

3. When you are perspiring heavily, it's time for an invigorating cold shower or plunge into a cold pool. This will also close your pores.

4. Your skin will now have cooled down, and you'll be ready for a few minutes more inside the sauna.

5. Finally, have another cold shower, followed by a brisk rub-down with a towel and you'll be refreshed and raring to go!

AFTER

● *Don't* go straight into something energetic – it's best to relax for a while.

● If you've coloured your hair recently – with henna, for example – you might notice droplets on your shoulders and towel (rather embarrassing if the towel doesn't belong to you!). I've also heard of it uncurling a perm!

RESULTS

You should feel very refreshed but a bit tired after a sauna, and your skin should be soft and glowing. You'll also notice a weight loss but this, unfortunately, will be replaced the minute you have a drink!

After a few saunas you should begin to notice an improvement in your skin, especially if you're prone to pimples etc.

ADDITIONAL FACTS

If you have saunas regularly, make sure you take lots of soft drinks to replace lost fluid and prevent dehydration.

MAN APPEAL? **Yes**	PLEASURE RATING **0**

SLENDERTONE

The Facts

WHAT IS IT?

Slendertone is a form of electro-muscular stimulation (EMS) which passively exercises and tones up the muscles. That is, you just lie there reading a magazine while a machine exercises your muscles for you!

Muscle stimulation has been used therapeutically in hospitals for around 130 years, but only around 20 years for cosmetic purposes. The principle dates back to the 18th century, when an Italian named Luigi Galvani discovered that applying a weak electric current to a frog's leg caused the muscles to contract and therefore exercise. This is because the current simulates the signals sent by the brain to the motor points of the muscles. By the 19th century Michael Faraday was using electric impulses to treat the muscles of injured racehorses so that even if they couldn't race again, they could breed and therefore protect their owners' vast investments.

Researchers at Slendertone have developed a simplified version of Faraday's original current which is low voltage (so that it's comfortable), as well as safe and efficient. It uses an interrupted pulse to fully shorten the muscle, with a specific relaxation time in between so that you don't get a build-up of lactic acid (which is what, with active exercise, makes you ache afterwards) or violent muscle fatigue. As a result, EMS is also referred to in some salons as 'faradism'.

WHERE CAN YOU TRY IT?
- In salons in almost every country
- In all health farms
- In some hotels
- At some fitness centres, where Slendertone is being combined with exercise.

HOW MUCH SHOULD IT COST?
From £5 to £10 per half hour, depending on the salon and the make of 'faradic' unit used. (Slendertone has become a generic name for EMS – as Hoover has for vacuum cleaner – so you may be offered another company's machine.)

For the top-of-the-range Slendertone 16, which has a specially developed TENS pulse (this anaesthetises the areas on which you place it, so that you can take a much stronger current), expect to pay top rates.

HOW OFTEN SHOULD YOU HAVE IT?
- Three times a week for three weeks.
- Alternatively, once a week for a month.

HOW LONG SHOULD A TREATMENT TAKE?
About thirty to forty-five minutes. The most effective treatment is between forty-five minutes and an hour, but most people don't like the idea of such a long session.

Any beauty salon that's offering an hour's treatment is offering very good value for money.

DO TRY SLENDERTONE:
1. if you're on a diet and want to avoid becoming saggy. Slendertone will not, however, help you lose weight: half an hour of Slendertone is the equivalent of a gentle half-hour stroll with the dog!
2. if you want to tone up healthy muscle.
3. if you're trying to lose inches. Results obtained can range from ½–3 inches/(1.25–7.5 cm)!
4. if you have back pain or muscular problems.
5. if you have piles (haemorrhoids). It's very effective, though most people are too embarrassed to ask for treatment for this problem. The same goes for a sagging uterus.
6. if you want to shorten a period – but not until after the fifth day.

7. after severe weight loss or childbirth (after two months). It's ideal for toning up muscles which have lost their elasticity.

DON'T TRY SLENDERTONE:
1. if you have a pacemaker. Slendertone will stop a standard one dead on impact.
2. if you have any nervous disease, such as epilepsy, multiple sclerosis or rheumatoid arthritis. The current going through the nerve fibres will stimulate the nerve and may increase the disease.
3. on the legs if you have varicose veins.
4. on the stomach on the first two days of your period – it will just increase the pain; or if you are pregnant – though you could use it on your legs to help counter fluid retention.
5. on a fresh scar, for example after a Caesarian section.
6. after you've had a baby, until you've stopped bleeding – about six to eight weeks.
7. if you're super-fit. If Sebastian Coe were to be put on a standard unit, he'd leap off the bench! That's because his muscles are so fit that the slightest stimulation would get to them.

HOW CAN YOU TELL IF A THERAPIST IS TRAINED?
Slendertone give qualified beauty therapists a one-day training course which deals with basic anatomy as well as electronic muscle stimulation (which they will have studied in depth at college).

Qualified Slendertone operators will display a Slendertone certificate; they will be able to analyse which areas are of concern to you and select the appropriate muscles to exercise and train.

WHAT SHOULD THE THERAPIST ASK YOU?
1. if you are fitted with a pacemaker.
2. if you are in good health.
3. if you can take normal exercise.
4. if you suffer from epilepsy.
5. if you have any form of nervous disease, eg multiple sclerosis, rheumatoid arthritis, etc.
6. if you have had any recent injury. If so, give details.
7. if you have varicose veins.
8. if you have a slipped disc.
9. if you have any inflamed areas.

WHAT SHOULD YOU ASK THE THERAPIST?
1. How she is padding you up. If the therapist doesn't under-

stand motor points and what she's doing, the treatment could be uncomfortable and not as effective as it should be.

Make sure she's keeping sets of pads on the same side of the body and not doing a lot of 'split padding'. If, for example, she puts one pad on one side of the leg and one on the other, she's actually not hitting anything at all because the muscles in most parts of the body run in an up-to-down position.

2. How long she is treating you for.

3. How many pads she will use. You should insist on getting all sixteen even if you only want to tone up, say, your tummy. Think how many muscles you use to hold in your tummy, for instance (buttocks, tummy, obliques and part of the thigh)! Besides, you're paying for a full treatment.

A Typical Slendertone Treatment ✍

BEFORE
- You shouldn't be wearing any oil, cream or powder.
- It's a good idea to have some sort of heat treatment first – eg radiated heat, sauna, infra-red, sunbed, hot shower or bath – since this heats up the body and improves circulation.
- You should drink a glass of water because, immediately after a treatment, you'll want to go to the loo.
- You shouldn't have a full meal directly before a treatment, otherwise it will interfere with your digestive process and make you feel sick.

DURING
1. The therapist will take your body measurements and assess which muscles need attention.

2. You'll lie down on a couch which has been prepared with Velcro-ed straps laid out to correspond with the selected body areas. They'll then be fastened fairly tightly so that they'll hold the conductive soft rubber pads, through which the weak electronic current is applied, firmly in place.

3. The pads will be thoroughly dampened before being placed under the straps. This is to make sure a good contact is made so that the Slendertone signal will flow freely to the muscle areas. It's perfectly safe.

4. All the pads should be carefully placed over the motor points – ie the small areas where nerves and muscles are most easily excited, and where you'll get a visible contraction with the minimum amount of stimulation.

You'll get a contraction even if the pad is not exactly over a motor point, but it won't be a maximum contraction.

5. The control unit will now be switched on and the signal on each pad adjusted until the correct degree of exercise is obtained.

Many people expect their limbs to twitch and jump about while they're having the treatment, and that it will be uncomfortable. In fact, you'll simply feel a tingling at first, then a quite definite rhythmic movement of the muscles which should not be unpleasant.

Incidentally, if you have layers of fat you won't be able to see anything happening at all; if you're fairly trim, though, you might be able to see muscles being flexed.

The area of the body which needs treatment should be padded up and turned on first. Once you've got a smooth contraction in

COPING WITH ANY SLENDERTONE PROBLEMS

Problems	Remedies
The treatment is uncomfortable.	Tell the therapist who will turn down the intensity or adjust the pads.
You're getting an unpleasant, prickling sensation.	The pads are not wet enough or they are dirty. Tell the therapist.
You've got any small areas of broken skin, or spots or erosions which are causing discomfort.	A piece of Elastoplast over the area will insulate the skin from the current.
The muscle pull is uneven or uncomfortable.	The pads are probably incorrectly placed. Tell the therapist.
You come out in a rash.	This is either because a) you're allergic to rubber; b) you've had some cream or oil on the body; or c) the pads are old or dirty. In future, ask for small circles of lint or towelling to be wetted and placed between the skin and the electrode pad so that treatment can be carried out. As a general rule, people who are likely to be allergic to rubber are those who are allergic to low grades of gold or junk jewellery. Allergies will go after a couple of days.

that area, the therapist should turn down the current while she pads up the rest of the body.

6. You'll be left to relax with a magazine for forty-five minutes or so. You'll find that you'll get used to the current after a short time, and you'll be able to take it stronger. The therapist should monitor you so that you get a balanced effect.

AFTER
- You should drink a glass of water or a vitamin drink.
- You'll feel as if you've had a relaxing little nap – frisky, tingly and raring to go – whereas after a heavy hour of aerobics or running you would feel washed out.
- You shouldn't ache. Aching is due to a build-up of lactic acid.

RESULTS
The effects of Slendertone treatments will last one and a half times as long as the effects of other forms of exercise. This is because the current fully shortens your muscle and gets it to a peak of fitness which you're not capable of doing yourself.

Home Care ✑

There's nothing to stop you buying a small Slendertone unit for use at home.

Further Information ✑

Slendertone's manufacturing company, Bio Medical Research, also produce units for medical use, so you can be sure that Slendertone machines are safe.

You *cannot* get a faradic burn from a Slendertone machine – ie a tiny red or brown mark, the size of a small nail head. This can only be caused by units whose manufacturing standards are poor.

If you get a burn you should immediately report it to the beauty salon, and *sue* the beauty salon – who will then sue the manufacturer. These burns will never go, and they will leave white scars.

The address of Slendertone Limited is:

8a London Road Tunbridge Wells, Kent, TN1 1DA. Tel: (0892) 46751.

They keep a list of every salon which has a Slendertone machine. If you ring up, they will tell you where your nearest salons are, how much they charge, their phone numbers and the kind of machines they have.

MAN APPEAL? **Yes** – Slendertone is especially good for men. It actually works faster and better on them since they have less layers of fat for the current to pass through!

PLEASURE RATING   −2

STEAM CABINET

The Facts

WHAT IS IT?
It is an upright metal cabinet in which steam circulates to cleanse and tone the skin as well as relax you. It's different to a sauna in that it uses moist heat instead of dry heat: in fact, a steam cabinet is rather like a traditional Turkish bath except that your head stays outside the steam.

WHERE CAN YOU TRY ONE?
- At beauty salons
- At health farms

HOW MUCH SHOULD IT COST?
From around £5.

HOW OFTEN SHOULD YOU HAVE ONE?
Up to two or three times a week.

HOW LONG SHOULD YOU STAY IN ONE?
Ideally, around ten to fifteen minutes – no longer than 25 minutes.

DO TRY A STEAM CABINET:
1. if you want a steam treatment where your head doesn't need to be enclosed.
2. to cleanse the skin.
3. as an aid to relaxation.
4. before a massage or certain body treatments such as aromatherapy.
5. to help ease tired muscles and joints.

DON'T TRY A STEAM CABINET:
1. if you are very nervous.
2. if you have acute eczema or any other flaking skin complaint.
3. if you are pregnant.
4. if you have high or low blood pressure.
5. if you have any respiratory problems such as bronchitis or asthma.
6. if you have any infectious disease.
7. if you suffer from epilepsy.
8. if you suffer from diabetes.
9. if you have any heart problems, especially a pacemaker.
10. if you have a back problem (there's nothing to rest your back on).

A Typical Steam Cabinet Treatment ✍

BEFORE
- Remove all jewellery.
- *Don't* use a steam cabinet directly after heavy exercise.

DURING
1. First of all, you'll be asked to undress. It's best to take off everything, though you could wear bikini bottoms if you prefer. The therapist will open the front of the cabinet and ask you to sit down inside. She'll adjust the seat to make sure you'll be comfortable when the door is closed.

   Your neck must be high enough to reach the neck of the cabinet, so if you're short and the seat is raised, make sure the therapist gives you something on which to rest your feet or you could end up with terrible backache. (As the back of the cabinet is slightly curved, there is nothing on which to lean.)
2. The therapist will then close the front of the cabinet, and place

towels around the neck opening, both to keep in the heat and for your comfort.

3. She'll then leave you to steam for ten to fifteen minutes, and if at any time you feel uncomfortable, shout! You'll get fairly hot and sweaty, as you're being bombarded with steam throughout the treatment, but it's not particularly unpleasant.

4. At the end of the treatment, she will open the front of the cabinet and put a towel around you. After all that heat you'll feel very chilly. You'll then be invited to have a cold shower – to restore the skin temperature to normal – though you may simply be left to towel yourself down before your next body treatment . . .

AFTER
● It's best to relax for a while.

RESULTS
You should feel very relaxed after a session in a steam cabinet, and your skin should be nice and smooth.

MAN APPEAL? Yes	PLEASURE RATING −2

SUNBEDS

The Facts

WHAT IS A SUNBED?
Despite warnings about the harmful effects of the sun's rays, many people still like to get a tan. And given the unpredictable climate in this country, that often means resorting to sunbeds.

If you want to use a sunbed there are safety precautions you can take to minimise any risk. First of all, make sure that any equipment you use conforms to BS3456 3.20 exposure limits – ie the safety limits for ultra-violet exposure levels on all suntanning equipment laid down by the British Standards Institute.

Secondly, remember that there are two kinds of ultra-violet rays found in natural sunlight – UVA and UVB. Modern sunbeds emit only UVA – the part of sunlight that tans without burning. *Never* use suntanning equipment that gives out high UVB: it can lead to a risk not only of painful sunburn but of long-term skin damage.

Finally, never exceed the recommended exposure time for your type of skin, and don't forget to wear goggles.

WHERE CAN YOU TRY ONE?
- At most salons
- At health farms and clubs
- At some hairdressers
- On board ships, etc
- At suntan centres

HOW MUCH SHOULD IT COST?
Prices vary considerably, depending on the kind of bed used. The

high-speed ones are most pricey per treatment, but you might find that since you will tan quicker it might work out cheaper in the long run.

HOW OFTEN SHOULD YOU HAVE A SUNBED TREATMENT?

This depends on your skin. Once a week if you have sensitive skin, once or twice a week if you have normal skin. Obviously, the more treatments you have, the better the tan, and a sensitive skin will take longer to tan.

HOW LONG SHOULD IT TAKE?

All sunbeds should give you a tan, but some will take longer than others. It depends on the kind of sunbed being used. On a high-speed sunbed, half an hour is ample for a normal skin which tans easily; on other beds you might be able to stay on for an hour. Since you're likely to get quite hot and uncomfortable lying still for so long, it might be better to have half an hour on a bed, then have a shower and go back for the second half hour.

If you have a sensitive skin you would only spend a few minutes under a high-speed sunbed.

DO TRY A SUNBED TREATMENT:

1. if you want an even tan without sun.
2. if you want to maintain your holiday tan.
3. if you want to build up a bit of colour before you expose your body on holiday – though remember you'll still need to take it *very* easy at first when you go out into the sunshine. Sunbeds will not prevent you from getting sunburnt!

Although UVA sunbeds do not protect your skin from sunlight, they do activate the skin's reaction to sunlight so you'll darken more speedily in sunlight if you've used UVA first.

DON'T TRY A SUNBED TREATMENT:

1. if you are on any kind of medication. The therapist will be able to advise you whether you can have a treatment, and may ask for your doctor's name and phone number so she can ring and check if she's in any doubt. If you have been on antibiotics, for example, you should leave a week before having a sunbed treatment or it could make you dizzy.
2. if you have any skin disorder, though UVA may be able to help eczema (check with your doctor first).
3. if you have ever had any radiation treatment.

4. if you are on the contraceptive pill. You could get uneven tanning.

5. if you are pregnant. It's not safe to have any kind of radiation treatment.

6. if you have a heart condition.

7. if you suffer from back problems. You could get very uncomfortable lying flat on a hard surface for a period of time.

8. if you suffer from epilepsy.

9. if you have a pacemaker or any other electrical equipment. The radiation could affect them.

10. if you've had an organ transplant.

11. if you have cataracts. It's not a good idea to try a sunbed, even wearing goggles.

12. if you suffer from migraines. The heat might make them worse.

13. if you have any moles.

14. if you have any kidney or urinary problems. The heat could encourage bacteria.

15. if you have diabetes. You can't feel the heat or heat changes.

16. if you usually suffer from sunburn, sunstroke or excessive peeling in the sun. You'll get the same under a sunbed.

17. if you are susceptible to heat rashes.

18. if you have sore eyes.

BEWARE OF LOTIONS AND POTIONS . . .

Unlike normal suntanning, you can't use any kind of suntan lotion when you're having a sunbed treatment. But your therapist might offer you a 'tanning accelerator' which is said to speed up the tanning process.

According to Frances Allwright, General Secretary of the Association of Sun Tanning Operators, a genuine accelerator works by increasing the skin's sensitivity to sunlight, so it's very easy to burn – even on a sunbed. The long-term disadvantages are much more serious. The ingredients used to accelerate tanning may cause marked thickening and ageing of the skin, and may even cause skin cancer if used regularly.

Many of the products, however, simply contain a harmless dye. You can check this by rubbing it on yourself before you go under the lamp. If your skin goes brown, it's not a genuine accelerator.

HOW CAN YOU TELL IF A THERAPIST/MACHINE/SALON IS GOOD?

1. The therapist will make sure you are comfortable during the session, returning at regular intervals to check on you.

2. A good salon will have an alarm button you can push if you need help, will have a cool-air fan in the cubicle, and will offer to switch on some music to while away the time. It's very boring lying in the dark in the same position, and half an hour can seem an eternity!

WHAT SHOULD YOU ASK THE THERAPIST?

What type of lamps are used and if they have high or low UVB output. If the therapist does not know, or if they are the high UVB type, go elsewhere.

A Typical Sunbed Session ✑

BEFORE

● You should have a shower, to wash off any perfume or creams you have applied. It's particularly important if you've just been swimming – the chlorine could affect the effects of the sunbed.

You can wash with soap during the shower – this will come off with the water – but you should not apply any body cream or make-up. If you leave perfume on the skin, you may not get any tan there, and you may get some irritation.

If you use cleanser and toner to remove make-up, it must be alcohol-free.

● You should remove contact lenses.

● You'll have to take off any jewellery – it could heat up and burn you. You also don't want your jewellery 'stencilled' on to your body!

DURING

1. You can wear as little or as much clothing as you like – but it's best not to wear anything at all if you want to get an even, all-over tan. (This is one of the few treatments where you're left in a room on your own, so you don't need to be embarrassed.) The therapist will probably leave you to get undressed first before returning to your cubicle to show you how to operate the machine.

2. You will be given a pair of dark goggles, which should be worn at all times. They're very tiny, so you shouldn't look like a panda when the treatment is over! Sunglasses are not a suitable alternative.

If you don't wear goggles you could get an infection, or cataracts. But if you have to take them off to find a button, don't panic – a few seconds without them shouldn't hurt.

It's a good idea to wear some kind of head covering to stop your hair drying out. If the salon doesn't provide one, ask for a towel to wrap around your hair (you could also take along a scarf).

3. The therapist will then show you how to operate the sunbed. Each machine is different, but all good ones will have buttons etc at arm's length. If you need something and can't find the button at any time, *shout*!

4. You'll then be asked to lie down on the bed, with a pillow under your head for comfort. The best sunbeds tan your back and front at the same time; on others the rays may come only from overhead so you may have to turn over half-way through the treatment.

For maximum effect, the overhead lamp should be positioned as near to your body as you can bear: say, around 6–8 inches (15–20 cm). You can always raise it during the treatment if you get nervous or feel claustrophobic. Good beds will only come to within a certain distance of your face, so you can't harm yourself.

Once you're comfortable, just lie back and dream of sun-kissed beaches . . .

5. At the end of the session, the machine will usually switch itself off; alternatively, the therapist will return to do it for you. You will then have a shower – you'll be very hot and sticky – and apply some moisturising lotion.

AFTER
- Just as with real sun, you might get the odd white mark where you've been lying oddly – for example, under your chin if you've sunbathed with your chin forwards.
- You might be a bit blotchy, but this will soon fade.

RESULTS
You should have the beginnings of a good tan . . .

Home Care ✑

If you're thinking of buying a sunbed, make sure you buy one with a UVB percentage of 0.5% or less. All reputable manufacturers will state this clearly in their literature. When used correctly, these lamps eliminate all risk of burning.

However, remember that, like the sun, too-frequent use of a sunbed may cause your skin to wrinkle.

Further Information ✒

Before embarking on a suntanning course, it's worth contacting ASTO, the Association of Sun Tanning Operators Ltd. This was formed by a group of salons and distributors all over the country who have set for themselves higher safety standards than current legislation dictates.

They will be able to give you details of the nearest salon on their register. They also run a free advisory service – manned by a team of experts – which is open twelve hours a day to give advice and help to anyone seeking advice on safety in suntanning.

Their address is:

The Association of Sun Tanning Operators Ltd 32 Grayshott Road, London SW11 5TT. Tel: 01-228 6077.

ASTO also produce some helpful literature dealing with suntanning under lamps and in real sunlight. Send a stamped, self-addressed envelope to ASTO at the above address for a free leaflet entitled *Safe Sun Tanning – Some Questions and Answers*. Another booklet, *Ultra-Violet Sun Tanning – Your Questions Answered*, costs £3 including postage and packing.

MAN APPEAL? **Yes**	PLEASURE RATING −2

THREAD VEIN TREATMENT

The Facts ✑

WHAT IS IT?

Thread veins – fine, broken veins – are most commonly found on the legs and the face, and occasionally on the neck. They appear for all sorts of reasons – for example, hormone changes or trauma, such as a kick from a horse – but they tend to run in families, particularly those who live in very hot or very cold climates. Smoking can make them worse, as can spicy food, lots of tea, coffee and alcohol – just think of an old wino in the street, with what used to be called 'grog blossoms' on his nose! Though thread veins aren't dangerous – they can't harm your health – they do develop and can look unsightly, which is why many people choose to have them treated.

There are two main methods of treatment – electrolysis, which cauterises the blood vessels, and sclerotherapy, started in 1953 by Katherine Corbett. Electrolysis is covered in detail on pages 51–61, so in this section I shall deal mainly with sclerotherapy.

Like electrolysis, sclerotherapy is a permanent treatment. If you have a tendency to thread veins, however, the treatment cannot prevent other veins appearing at a later date. It is used on both the face and legs, unlike electrolysis, which is most successful on the face.

Sclerotherapy actually means 'shrinking'. A chemical called STD – sodium tetradecyl sulphate, a very diluted form of the drug used on varicose veins, is injected into the veins to shrink them. This pushes the blood out into the tissues, causing a bruise which is gradually reabsorbed, and eventually the veins disappear.

WHERE CAN YOU HAVE A THREAD VEIN TREATMENT?
- at beauty salons (electrolysis)
- at health farms (electrolysis)
- at specialist clinics, staffed by trained nurses (sclerotherapy)

HOW MUCH SHOULD IT COST?
Sclerotherapy will cost around £50 per session; electrolysis from around £15 per session. Since only a small area can be treated at a time with electrolysis, there's probably little difference in the final cost of eliminating thread veins.

HOW OFTEN SHOULD YOU HAVE SCLEROTHERAPY?
This depends on the area to be treated. If you have just one small patch you might be able to get away with just one treatment. But on average you'll need four to five sclerotherapy treatments for legs, fewer for faces. Some people also respond much better than others.

You'll have to leave six weeks between treatments to allow all the bruising to die down.

HOW LONG SHOULD IT TAKE?
Sclerotherapy treatments usually last for half an hour; see page 51 for electrolysis details. Therapists tend to do less extensive sclerotherapy on the face than the legs at one time simply because it's quite traumatic having a lot of bruising on the face.

DO HAVE THREAD VEIN TREATMENT:
- if you have any kind of broken veins and are self-conscious about them.
- if you are over sixteen.

DON'T HAVE SCLEROTHERAPY:
- if the veins are very fine and scattered, as they won't respond so well – and you can't use sclerotherapy as a preventative treatment.
- if you've got an active skin problem such as rosacea. This is a disorder of the capillaries and you may need antibiotics.
- if you are pregnant.

(See pages 53–4 for when not to have Electrolysis.)

WHAT WILL THE THERAPIST ASK YOU?

1. How long you've had the thread veins, whether they've just appeared, or have developed over a number of years. If caused by trauma – such as a knock on your leg – hopefully they won't reappear after treatment.

2. Whether anything, in your knowledge, makes them worse – eg sudden temperature changes, a boozy night out etc.

3. Whether you are on the pill. That could be the cause, in which case it may be better to come off the pill first and see if the veins improve before spending money on treatment.

Other hormonal changes – such as the menopause or pregnancy – can also cause thread veins.

4. Whether you have had a dramatic weight loss. This could cause thread veins.

5. Whether you wax your legs. This is thought to contribute to leg thread veins.

WHAT SHOULD YOU ASK THE THERAPIST?

1. Whether she uses disposable needles. Nurses carrying out sclerotherapy should wear rubber gloves and gowns, and use all disposable equipment. It is also important to ask about disposable needles when having electrolysis for thread veins.

2. How many treatments will you need, and the cost? It's quite an expensive treatment so you'll have to be happy you can afford the whole course.

A Typical Sclerotherapy Face Vein Treatment ✒

BEFORE

- You'll be asked to come in for a consultation so that the therapist can assess how many treatments you will need.
- You'll be warned that this is a bruisable treatment – you'll be left with marks on your face for about a week – so you must make sure you've planned it properly from a social point of view.
- If you are prone to allergic reactions, the therapist may do a patch test.
- Don't arrive plastered with make-up.

DURING

1. You'll be asked to lie on a couch and covered with towels. Your

skin will then be cleaned with spa water, and tissue-wrapped ice will be smoothed across the areas requiring treatment to prepare the skin. Ice helps deaden the area, too, as the treatment can be quite uncomfortable in certain places, particularly around the nostrils.

2. Through a magnifying lamp the therapist will select a network of veins: they're all interconnected with each other so it doesn't mean that every single vein has to be injected.She will also use the magnifying lamp to see how far the chemical has travelled.

3. The therapist will then cover your eyes with eyepads, or ask you to shut your eyes so you don't have to watch the needle (and also to avoid any chemical getting in your eyes). Then she'll inject the vein using a tiny needle.

The chemical might begin to sting around 30 seconds after it has entered the vein. Some people, however, say they don't feel anything at all! But it wears off very quickly. You could also get some spontaneous bruising and swelling, particularly if the therapist is treating an area near the eyes.

For a bad thread vein case on the face you might get around eight injections on each side, plus a selection on the nose, but it's all very quick. There will, however, be a bit of 'bleedback': once you've punctured the little capillary it will bleed, so the therapist will apply a little bit of pressure with a tissue.

4. Once the therapist has completed all the injections, you'll feel very hot, and your face will feel as if it's throbbing a bit.

5. A piece of tissue, saturated with spa water, will now be placed on the face – it's very soothing. The therapist may also wipe some ice over the area. You'll be given a cup of reviving tea, and left until the tissue is dry.

6. Finally, the therapist will clean you up and apply some tinted powder, which does quite a good job of covering up the bruises.

AFTER

● You'll have purple bruises in the areas that have been treated a day or two after the treatment. With some people these bruises last for quite some time, others find theirs fade quickly. (On legs, bruises are brown rather than purple.)

● You won't be at all incapacitated. Dancers with thread veins on their legs have pirrhouetted on stage a few hours after a treatment!

● You might be a little swollen afterwards, but all you need to do is apply some ice.

● You shouldn't wear moisturiser or make-up for ten days, as you don't know what's in your creams and you could have a nasty interaction of cream and chemical. You could, however, wear tinted antiseptic powder, which you can buy at the salon.

If you must wear eye make-up, be very careful when taking it off.

● You should spray sterile sulphur spa water on to the area night and morning, and use antiseptic powder as often as required.

● Avoid any rubbing or friction to the skin.

● Don't use elastoplast dressing on or near the area.

● If you've had treatment on leg veins, don't go swimming in a chlorinated pool for at least seven days, and avoid body lotions, bath essences and suntan lotions for two weeks. You can, however, take baths.

You should also avoid leg waxing, shaving and rubbing the legs for at least ten days.

RESULTS

The veins that are treated will not come back, but that's not to say that if you have a tendency to thread veins they won't appear *round* the treated area.

Further treatments will be less uncomfortable as you get used to the sensation.

Further Information ✎

Sclerotherapy – which is carried out by trained nurses – is only available at:

The Katherine Corbett Clinic, First Floor, 21 South Molton Street, London, W1Y 1DD. Tel: 01-629 6136.

Rosalind Bendall Beauty Clinic, 27 Wellington Way, Waterlooville, Hants, PO7 7ED. Tel: Waterlooville 262 508.

For details of qualified therapists using electrolysis, contact BABTAC (see page 11).

MAN APPEAL?   **Yes** – for bad broken veins on noses and faces.

PLEASURE RATING   −5

TOP-TO-TOE TREATMENT

The Facts

WHAT IS IT?
Many salons offer a 'package' of different treatments, which might include a manicure, pedicure, massage, facial, eyebrow tidy-up and sunbed session, for an all-inclusive price.

The advantage of this kind of package is that the treatments can and should complement one another.

WHERE CAN YOU TRY IT?
- At some beauty salons
- At some hairdressers which offer beauty treatments
- At certain health farms

HOW MUCH SHOULD IT COST?
It depends on the treatments included – expect to pay anything from around £30.

HOW OFTEN SHOULD YOU HAVE IT?
Whenever you fancy a treat.

HOW LONG SHOULD IT TAKE?
Depends on the package – anything from half a day to a day.

DO TRY A TOP-TO-TOE TREATMENT:
1. a day or two before a special occasion – perhaps your wedding!

If the package includes a facial, or any treatment that will mess up your hair, see if you can have your hair styled at the end. You'll enjoy the day even more if you come away looking well groomed as well as healthy and relaxed.

2. if you simply fancy a treat.

3. if you're recovering from illness and need something to buck you up – but do check that all treatments included in the package are suitable. (If not, see if unsuitable ones can be changed for something else.)

4. to get the chance to try out a selection of treatments.

5. to get an idea of what a stay at a health farm might be like, before parting with a great deal of money.

MAN APPEAL?   Depends what's included in the package.

PLEASURE RATING   +5 if you don't have far to travel, +3 if you do!

VACUUM SUCTION

The Facts

WHAT IS IT?
The object of this treatment is to convey softened fat cells in the lymph to the nearest lymphatic glands and help them disperse. As well as draining excess fluid, vacuum suction will remove impurities from your system.

The machines use clear plastic cups with flattened edges (which will not bruise the tissues), attached to a kind of 'vacuum cleaner'. As you are 'vacuumed' you'll see the fat you're hoping to get rid of lift and move along the body!

WHERE CAN YOU TRY IT?
- At some beauty salons
- At health farms
- At some slimming clinics

HOW MUCH SHOULD IT COST?
From around £5 a treatment.

HOW OFTEN SHOULD YOU HAVE IT?
Once a week for a course of around ten treatments to see any results.

HOW LONG SHOULD IT TAKE?
Around thirty minutes.

DO HAVE A VACUUM SUCTION:
1. if you have excessive soft fat – for example, on thighs, tummy, buttocks, back, neck, shoulders, face, arms – you want to get rid of.
2. in conjunction with diet and possibly other slimming treatments.
3. after a severe weight loss – it may help tighten up saggy skin.

DON'T HAVE VACUUM SUCTION:
1. if you've recently had any major operation.
2. if you have any recent scar tissue or open wounds.
3. on the legs if you have varicose veins.
4. if you are pregnant (though it can be used fairly soon after childbirth – your therapist should advise you).
5. if you have any heart problems.
6. if you suffer from any medical condition (check with your doctor first).
7. if you have a pacemaker or metal plates.

A Typical Vacuum Suction Treatment ✍

BEFORE
• It's best not to have a heavy meal.

DURING
1. You will be asked to undress, down to your knickers probably. You'll then lie down on your back on a couch, and the therapist will cover your body with towels except for the area being treated.
2. She will then apply oil to the area to help the cup glide along the skin. After selecting the right cup for that particular area she will switch the machine on to the lowest setting, place the cup on the outer side of the area to be treated, then she'll gradually increase the suction until the cup is half-full with flesh.
  You'll feel a suction–lifting sensation: if it feels too uncomfortable, tell the therapist to turn the suction down.
3. She will lift the cup away from the skin and carry it slowly – gliding – along the skin to the nearest lymphatic glands. On reaching them, she will tip the cup and depress the skin with her little finger to break off the suction.
  She'll then repeat it with as many strokes as she feels neces-

sary. She mustn't push the cup along the skin or you may get slight bruising.

4. She could do anything from ten to twenty-five strokes on each section, but on the face only eight to ten strokes.

AFTER

- You might look a little red – this will go down in a few minutes.
- Your skin should feel nice and soft.
- You might feel a slight tingling sensation where your circulation has been increased.

RESULTS

Vacuum suction should help get rid of some surplus softened fat.

MAN APPEAL?   **Yes** – it may help after a severe weight loss.

PLEASURE RATING   **−2**

WAXING

The Facts

WHAT IS IT?

Waxing is a temporary method of hair removal using wax, which is applied in strips. The hair sticks to the wax as it dries, and is yanked out when the therapist pulls off the strips. It can be used to remove hair from the upper lip, chin, underarms, arms, legs and bikini line.

Despite the fact that this isn't the most pleasant of treatments, waxing was found in a recent survey to be the most popular and most requested beauty treatment, which shows the importance British women place on hair removal!

Unlike electrolysis (see page 51) which will eventually destroy unwanted hair altogether, waxed hairs will grow back within a few weeks. The advantage of waxing over electrolysis, however, is that large areas can be treated in one session.

Waxing is also much more successful than shaving, for two reasons. The first is that regrowth is much slower: if you shave your legs you'll start to feel prickly in a day or two, but with waxing you can expect to have smooth legs for up to six weeks. That is because waxing takes away the whole hair shaft from the follicle, whereas shaving simply removes any hair visible above the surface of the skin. Secondly, the hair will grow back with a fine end, not a blunt one as with shaving, so you won't have any unpleasant stubble.

In time, the hair should get visibly finer, and may even eventually stop growing – though this depends on the original thickness of the hair and whether you've been creaming or shaving the hair (which will have made it coarser).

WHERE CAN YOU TRY IT?
- At most salons
- At health farms and clubs
- On board ships, etc
- At some hairdressing salons

HOW MUCH WILL IT COST?
This varies considerably depending on the products used and the amount of hair to be removed. Expect to pay anything from £3 upwards for a lip wax, from £10 for a full leg wax.

HOW OFTEN SHOULD YOU HAVE IT DONE?
Whenever hair is long enough – about ¼ inch (6 mm). This should be around every four to six weeks.

HOW LONG SHOULD IT TAKE?
This depends on whether the hairs all manage to attach themselves to the wax. Strays will have to be plucked out, which can make the treatment longer. But this is a relatively quick treatment. A leg wax, for example, may well take no longer than fifteen minutes.

DO TRY WAXING:
1. if you have unwanted hair but don't want to try electrolysis.
2. if you want hair-free legs for the duration of your holiday. Have your legs waxed a couple of days before you leave.
3. if you want to avoid the stubble (and, under arms, the dark patches) you get after shaving.

DON'T TRY WAXING:
1. if you are diabetic – your skin will be thinner.
2. if you suffer from epilepsy.
3. if you have any skin disease.
4. if you are prone to allergies. If you are, you could ask the therapist to do a small patch test to see if you have any allergic reaction. You shouldn't have to pay for this.
5. if you are currently having your period as you will be very sensitive.
6. if you have blonde hair. You'll find the hairs getting darker eventually, and the same applies if you shave blonde hair.

HOW CAN YOU TELL IF A THERAPIST IS GOOD?
1. She will minimise the discomfort by ripping the strips off very quickly, perhaps distracting you by talking.
2. She will also make sure the strips are always removed against the direction of hair growth. If you look at your legs closely you'll notice that hair on different sections grows in different directions, so if the therapist applies all the strips in the same direction you can be fairly certain she's not doing her job correctly.

A Typical Half-Leg Wax Treatment Using Cool Wax ✍

BEFORE
● Hair should be fairly long before waxing – at least ¼ inch (6 mm) so that the wax can grip it.
● *Don't* have a hot bath.
● *Don't* go for a treatment wearing jeans or trousers – your legs may be a little sensitive afterwards and it may be more comfortable to wear a loose skirt.

DURING
1. You'll be asked to take off your tights, skirt and slip. The therapist will then start by cleaning your legs with pads of cotton wool soaked in surgical spirit to make sure there's no grease on them (otherwise the wax won't stick). For a bikini wax, you can keep your pants on – the therapist will simply pull them up slightly and put tissue around the edges.
2. The wax is applied with a spatula in the direction of the hair growth. Then strips of specially prepared paper – rather like blotting paper – are pressed on top, one by one.
  Cool wax is quicker and less messy than hot wax, as well as being more hygienic. Cool wax isn't recycled – it's thrown away – whereas hot wax (except for bikini and underarm wax) is melted down and has the hairs strained out of it so that it can be used again and again.
  Cool wax, incidentally, is a misnomer: it's kept at a constant temperature of around 48°C/118°F, although it tends to feel hotter as the treatment progresses and your legs begin to feel rather more sensitive.
3. As the strips are quickly ripped off, away from the hair growth, they take the wax off – and the hair with it. The treatment

is not particularly comfortable, but each burst of discomfort lasts only a second, so it's not too bad.

You'll be reassured to learn, though, that some women actually fall asleep during a treatment once they get used to the sensation!
4. The therapist will pluck any stray hairs, and finally apply a soothing lotion.

AFTER
● Legs may be a bit red and blotchy afterwards, which is a natural reaction. The redness will last for anything between ten minutes and a few hours, depending on the individual.
● With underarm and bikini waxing, you may develop blood spots, which is quite normal as the hair is so deep rooted. These too will go away on their own.
● *Don't* go swimming for at least 24 hours.
● *Don't* wear any body make-up for 24 hours.
● *Don't* sunbathe directly afterwards.
● *Don't* have a hot bath for a few hours.
● *Don't* wear tights or stockings. Let the air get to your legs for an hour or two.
● After an underarm wax, *don't* wear deodorant for 24 hours as your pores will be open.
● *Don't* wear tight underwear or jeans directly after a bikini wax.

RESULTS
Your skin should stay smooth and hairless for up to six weeks. You may, however, notice stray hairs growing during this time. These will be new hairs, not the ones which were removed.

Home Care ✍

In between treatments, try to avoid shaving as it may encourage hair to grow back more coarsely and to lie in different directions. This will make waxing harder.

In addition, if you shave or use a depilatory cream between waxing treatments, you will not give hair the chance to grow sufficiently long for it to be waxed!

MAN APPEAL? **Not really** PLEASURE RATING −4

HOME BEAUTY TIPS

- Store tubes of cream standing on their caps so there's no air lock.

- Always replace the tops on bottles, and store them in a cool dry place, out of sunlight and not near a radiator. They'll last longer.

- Don't expect to buy every product the therapist advises. Start by asking her which are most urgent. You can always add to the range afterwards.

- Before you buy any product, try it out during a treatment. Or ask the salon if you can have a free sample to try.

- Always use an exfoliating product over the bathroom sink to avoid unnecessary mess.

- Consider investing in an eye gel which is wonderfully soothing, and will reduce puffiness around the eyes in the morning. Apply it with the tip of your ring finger from the nose, across the brow bone and back under the eyes, to avoid stretching the delicate skin in the area. Blot it if you've been a bit heavy-handed.

- When using a face mask, always avoid the eye area. You could end up with puffy eyes or other irritation.

- When applying cream or a lotion, always put it into the palms of your hands first. This will take the chill off, and emulsify the product so it will go on the skin evenly.

- When using any face products, don't stop under the chin, but continue down the neck area. This will help prevent lines and discoloration.

- If you use a peel-off mask, try applying a thicker strip around the outside of your face so you'll have something to grip when you take the mask off.

• You should start using eye products as soon as you start wearing make-up.

• Ask your therapist's advice on any beauty problems – how to reduce puffiness, improve circulation etc. She will be able to recommend products which may help.

• Get rid of hard skin on elbows etc with a body exfoliating cream. Have a good rub, then a bath.

• Treat your legs to a soothing massage. It'll make your skin wonderfully smooth and will improve circulation. Invest in a small bottle of aromatherapy oil. The Body Shop do a full range and you should get four to five treatments out of their tiny bottles. Neroli or rose is ideal if you're tired and achey; lavender is good for rheumatism and arthritis; camomile is very relaxing; and peppermint will also clear your breathing if you have a cold!

Run some hot tap water and fill a small bowl with it. Place the jar of oil – still with its cap on – in the water to warm the oil through. It doesn't need to be hot, just slightly warm. Work a little into your legs (and your elbows if you like). The warmth of the oil and the aroma should be wonderfully therapeutic and relaxing.

• After a hard day on your feet, or when you've been out shopping, fill a bowl with warm water and bubble bath or Radox, make yourself a cup of tea, pick up a book or magazine and soak your feet for twenty minutes. Then rub some body lotion on your feet – you'll feel so much better!

• Use a damp sponge to apply foundation – it'll go on more smoothly.

• Invest in a night cream, whatever your age. It's richer than a day cream and will work on your skin overnight. Tissue off any excess. And don't forget to apply it to your neck, too!

INTERNATIONAL
ADDRESS BOOK

Major Beauty Organisations Around the World ✍

AUSTRALIA
Advanced Association of Beauty Therapists, GPO Box 2885, 2001 Sydney

Australian Federation of Aestheticians & Beauty Therapists, Box 2078, GPO Brisbane 4001, Australia

AUSTRIA
Im Haus Oest. Gewerbevereines, Exchenbachgasse 11, A-1010 Vienna

BRAZIL
Federacao Brasileira d'Estetica e Cosmetologia, Rua Barao da Torre, 446-Ipanema, 22411 Rio de Janeiro

CANADA
Association of Professional Aestheticians of Ontario, P.O. Box 6384, Postal Section A, Toronto MSW 1X3, Ontario

Canadian International Esthetics Association, 829-470 Granville Street, Vancouver B.C. V6C 1VS, Canada

DENMARK
Dansk Kosmetologforening, Kastanajevej 41, DK-2840 Holte, Denmark

FINLAND
Suomen Cidesco Ry, Sammonkatu 7 A, SF-00100 Helsinki

GERMANY
Cidesco Deutschland, Kaiserstrasse 7, D-6600 Saarbrucken 3

GREAT BRITAIN
British Association of Beauty Therapy & Cosmetology, Suite 5, Wolseley House, Oriel Road, Cheltenham, Glos. GL50 1TH, England

Independent Professional Therapists International, Storcroft House, London Road, Retford, Notts, England

National Federation of Health & Beauty Therapists, P.O. Box 36, Arundel, West Sussex, BN18 0SW, England

GREECE
Hellas Cidesco, 13–15 Sotiros Street, Piraeus 18535, Greece

HONG KONG
Cicesco Section, 16 Granville Road, 3rd Floor, Kowloon, Hong Kong

ICELAND
Felag Islenzkra Snyrifraedinga, P.O. Box 315, 121 Reykjavik

INDONESIA
Cidesco Section, Jl. K.H. Mahmud 5, RW 02/Rt. 0011, Jakarta-Selatan 12780, Indonesia

IRELAND
Society of Applied Cosmetology, 40 Grafton Street, Dublin 2

ISRAEL
Cosmeticians Association of Israel, P.O. Box 4041, Tel Aviv

JAPAN
Cidesco Nippon, Kitamura Building, 3-17-5 Ueno, Taito-ku, Tokyo

MALAYSIA
Malaysian Beauty Therapy Association, 16B Jalan 19/36, Petaling Jaya

NETHERLANDS
ANBOS, Erasmusweg 1559, NL-2542 PB, The Hague

NEW ZEALAND
Cidesco Section, 291 St. Heliers Bay Road, Auckland 5

The Association of Beauty Therapists of New Zealand, P.O. Box 28-026, Remeura, Auckland 5

NORWAY
Norske Kosmetologers Forbund, Torgatan 10, Oslo 1

PUERTO RICO
Ass. Esteticstas, 73 Santiago Inglesias Street, Condado, Puerto Rico 00907

SINGAPORE
Singapore Association of Beauty Therapists, 04-12 & 13 Far East Plaza, Scotts Road, Singapore 0922

SOUTH AFRICA
South African Institute of Beauty Therapists, P.O. Box 56318, Pinegowrie 2123

SWEDEN
Svenska Hudterapeuters Riksforbund, Drakslingan 6, 19300 Sigtuna

UNITED STATES OF AMERICA
Aestheticians International Association Inc., 5206 McKinney, Dallas, Texas

Cidesco U.S.A., 1440 Canal Street, Suite 812, New Orleans, Louisiana 70112

Skin Care Association of America, 1009 West Chester Pike, West Chester PA 19382